Controll

03

.003

104

104

2004

2006
2006

Controlling Anxiety

*Self-help strategies to conquer
fear and phobias and live
with confidence*

WILLIAM STEWART

2nd edition

How To Books

By the same author in this series

Building Self-Esteem
Self-Counselling
Going for Counselling (with Angela Martin)
Learning to Counsel (with Jan Sutton)

Published by How To Books Ltd,
3 Newtec Place, Magdalen Road,
Oxford OX4 1RE, United Kingdom.
Tel: (01865) 793806. Fax: (01865) 248780.
email: info@howtobooks.co.uk
http://www.howtobooks.co.uk

First edition 1998
Second edition 2000

British Library Cataloguing in Publication Data.
A catalogue record for this book is available from
the British Library.

Cover design by Shireen Nathoo Design
Cover image by PhotoDisc

Produced for How To Books by Deer Park Productions
Typeset by Kestrel Data, Exeter
Printed and bound by Cromwell Press Ltd, Trowbridge, Wiltshire

NOTE: The material contained in this book is set out in good
faith for general guidance and no liability can be accepted
for loss or expense incurred as a result of relying in particular
circumstances on statements made in the book. Laws and
regulations are complex and liable to change, and readers should
check the current position with the relevant authorities before
making personal arrangements.

Contents

List of Illustrations

Preface
to the Second Edition

This book is written primarily as a self-help book. Many people suffer from anxiety, often mild, but sometimes crippling. This is not a textbook on mental illness, although much of what will be discussed does come under the umbrella of mental health. The book is written for the person in the street, and not in technical language.

As Dr Claire Weekes said in her book *Self Help for your Nerves*: 'Many of those who suffer from nervousness are persons of fine sensibilities, of delicate regard for honour, endowed with a feeling of duty and obligation. Their nerves have tricked and misled them.'

This is the stance I have taken in dealing with people who suffer from anxiety and, indeed, other mental health problems. The seeds of anxiety, depression and any other of what we call mental illness, lie within us all. The fact that we can feel jittery about taking an exam, or feel 'blue' when things are not going right, or we can't stop crying when someone dies, or we think someone is getting at us, all indicate that we have the potential to experience full-blown mental illness. None of us is so superior that we are immune from the traumas of life. If up to now we have not suffered crippling anxiety, or depression that sucks us into the depths of despair, or obsessions that torture our waking hours and torment our dreams with terror, then we should count ourselves very fortunate. At the same time, let us not be complacent and think that it will never happen. None of us knows what is round the corner of life. None of us knows how we will cope with, for example, the sudden death of a loved one.

I do not talk about 'cure', but of finding the strength within to rise above whatever is causing the anxiety. My belief is that if we can turn the anxiety indicator down at least one notch, then life will be lived with more pleasure and satisfaction.

'The strength to recover is within you, once you are shown the way.' My sincere hope is that Dr Weekes' words will find an echo in your heart if you are desperately searching for some ways of making sense of what is happening in your life. If you work with people who are suffering, then I hope that this book will help you to help them.

Although I believe that all people who suffer from anxiety will find benefit from reading this and other self-help books, when anxiety is chronic, or when it interferes with normal activity, the sufferer is in need of medical help which goes beyond the remit of this book.

Feeling anxious, or any of the variations talked about in this book, is nothing to be ashamed of, any more than it would be if you developed pneumonia. Feeling crippled by anxiety is not a sign of weakness. It does not mean that you are immature, nor that you are a hopeless case. You may feel hopeless; you may feel constantly under threat of something you cannot identify, so much so that you fear you are going mad. Take notice of these feelings, for these are what your doctor needs to hear. The more you can tell your GP, the more informed his or her choices will be when it comes to offering you help.

Above all, when things look the blackest they have ever looked, remember this: you are a very important person. Whatever your life story is, however traumatic or disturbed, you are still important. Someone, somewhere, needs you, and whatever you are passing through right now, think on this: you *are* passing through and you will come out the other side. You have a contribution to make to society which only you can make. That is why you are a very important person.

I am indebted to Neil Morrison of the Institute of Counselling, Glasgow, for permission to use some of the material from two of the Institute's distance learning courses: *Introduction to Stress Management* (1996) and *Psychology for Counsellors* (1996).

William Stewart

IS THIS YOU?

Feeling anxious most of the time   Always living in the past

Experiencing sexual problems

Troubled by stress   Struggling with illness

Anxious about work

Coping with bereavement   Prone to irrational thinking

Beset by fears

Lacking direction in life   Wanting to run away from it all

Suffering low self-esteem

Facing major life changes   Overwhelmed with worry

Lacking belief in yourself

Often down in the dumps   Worried by sleeplessness

Having thoughts of suicide

Plagued by negative thoughts   Weary from being a carer

Struggling with conflicts

Often feeling low   Finding change difficult

Beset by panic attacks

Drained of energy   Worried by obsessions

Controlled by guilt

Ruled by a phobia   Having worries about eating

1

Assessing Your Knowledge of Anxiety

Anxiety is a distressing feeling of uneasiness, apprehension, or dread. Anxiety as a physical and emotional response to a fear may be rational, based on an actual event, or irrational, based on an anticipated event which may, or may not, take place, and when no appropriate action is finally taken.

A certain amount of unrealistic and irrational mild anxiety is part of most people's experience, and seems to be an unavoidable part of human personality. Indeed, unwelcome and uncomfortable emotions are expected, commonplace experiences in the everyday lives of most people.

Very often these feelings are made worse by dwelling on the fear of what the emotions might mean. Generally the fear is of some terrible illness or disease.

> **At a deeper level anxiety is** *a fear of non-being,*
> **which may be fear of death, but also a sense of**
> **meaninglessness and a powerful sense of guilt.**

Anxious people are in suspense, waiting for something, they know not what. A main source of anxiety is the fear of being separated from other persons who are felt to provide security.

IDENTIFYING THE CHARACTERISTICS OF ANXIOUS PEOPLE

Anxious people display the following characteristics:

- They are always on the alert.
- They over-react to noise.
- They feel helpless in the face of actual or imagined danger.
- Their moods alternate between hope and despair.

Some typical indicators of anxiety are:

- skin pallor
- sweating, or, less often, flushed
- sweat on the upper lip and forehead
- sweaty palms
- dry mouth
- dilated pupils
- increased pulse/heart rate and breathing
- mild exertion produces undue increase in heart rate
- muscle tension
- dizziness, or light feelings in the head
- tightness in the chest and throat
- stomach feels 'knotted'
- there may be diarrhoea and/or vomiting
- sinking feelings in the abdomen
- desire to pass water frequently
- limbs feel like jelly
- loss of sexual interest or inability to have sex.

IDENTIFYING LEVELS OF ANXIETY

Not all events that produce feelings of anxiety are necessarily unpleasant. Getting married or being presented with an award are two events that could be termed pleasant; yet they often produce feelings of anxiety. Generally, however, the anxiety associated with such events is not long-lasting, and feelings usually return to normal quite quickly, in much the same way as the heart rate, in a healthy individual, returns to normal after exercise.

Normal anxiety, in small amounts, is biologically necessary for survival. Anxiety in doses too large for us to handle leads to panic, and panic produces irrational behaviour. Panic is more likely to be caused by **free-floating anxiety** – anxiety that cannot be readily attributed to any specific event or idea. It is there, constantly lurking in the background. When it attacks, the person is once again set a-running on the treadmill. When anxiety is chronic, and not traceable to any specific cause, or when it interferes with normal activity, the sufferer is in need of expert help.

Feeling helpless and indecisive

Free-floating anxiety is characterised by trembling, jitteriness, tension, sweating, light-headedness, feelings of apprehension and irritability. It frequently manifests itself as the result of opposing or conflicting wishes, desires, beliefs, life events, or strain resulting from conflict between roles. The more desperate the feeling of helplessness and indecision, and the more difficult the decision between two opposing forces, the more severe the anxiety. Anxiety may show itself in:

- depression

- hopelessness

- powerlessness

- poor self-esteem/self-worth.

HIGHLIGHTING ANXIETY-PRODUCING SITUATIONS

Some typical events that generate anxiety are:

1. Tests, examinations, medical appointments.
2. Meeting deadlines.
3. Meeting important people.
4. Interviews.
5. Waiting for a baby to be born.
6. Driving test.
7. Being involved in a traffic accident.
8. Hearing bad news.
9. Relationships with:
   —spouse (partner)
   —parents
   —children
   —work colleagues
   —someone new.

EXERCISE

Identifying anxiety-producing events

1. What incidents in your life do you associate with any of the above situations? These may be places you have visited; people you have met; events; situations in which you were involved. You may think of others that are not listed.
2. Do you feel more anxious about actual or anticipated events?
3. Can you remember the first time you experienced these feelings?
4. Did you feel like this when you:
   - started school?
   - were punished for something?
   - started your first job?
   - were waiting at the wedding altar?
   - went to a funeral of a friend/relative?
   - took your first aeroplane trip?
   - were admitted to hospital?

UNDERSTANDING THE TREADMILL OF ANXIETY

Anxiety is both a prison and a punishment. Those who experience severe anxiety are trapped within a process over which they seem to have no control, in the same way that a prisoner would be subjected to the treatmill. There the pace was set by a gaoler. If he felt particularly vindictive, a turn on the control lever increased the pace at which the prisoner was forced to run. There was no respite, no escape. Exhaustion was inevitable. This is the picture of the outcome of anxiety; a state from which the victim may not escape unless some influence can be brought to bear on the gaoler to slow the rate at which the mill turns and allow the prisoner to step out onto firm ground.

Seeing the effect of anxiety

One of the characteristics of anxiety is that the more severe it is, the more it erodes every aspect of the person's life. The more this happens, the less able is the person to function effectively. The person's total psychic energy is swamped with the anxious feelings. Thinking becomes unclear, and problem-solving ability is impaired. The inner struggle, the constant feeling of pressures, coupled with the feeling of not coping, leads to exhaustion and defeat. The prisoner collapses on the floor of the treadmill, while the gaoler laughs.

Who is the gaoler? The gaoler is whatever, or whoever, it is that seeks to drive the person on to exhaustion. This may be a punitive conscience, guilt, ambition, fear of failure, or one of a multitude of fears. It is possible that there are multiple gaolers, each of whom may be at war with the others. The resultant conflict increases the tension felt by the victim.

Accompanying disorders
Many people have a single anxiety disorder and nothing else, but it isn't unusual for an anxiety disorder to be accompanied by another illness, such as **depression**, an **eating disorder, alcoholism, drug abuse**, or another anxiety disorder. Often people who have **panic disorder** or **social phobia**, for example, also experience the intense sadness and hopelessness associated with depression or become dependent on alcohol. In such cases, these problems will need to be treated as well.

IDENTIFYING COMMON ANXIETY AND STRESS-RELATED SYMPTOMS

Signs and symptoms of anxiety are heightened during times of stress. This is possibly because stress lowers our resistance, and what would normally not be a problem assumes frightening proportions. During times of stress, for example when someone dies, our normal defence mechanisms are weakened, allowing anxiety to surface. Fatigue often leads to anxiety and is caused by trying to spread ourselves around too thinly. Signs and symptoms include:

anger	backaches
chronic constipation	chronic diarrhoea
fatigue	fears
headaches	hostility
high blood pressure	indigestion
insomnia	irritability
irritable bowel	muscle spasms
muscular tension	neck aches
nightmares	obesity
obsessions	phobias

physical weakness	resentment
sexual difficulties	sleeping difficulties
tics	tremors
ulcers	unwanted thoughts.

KNOWING THE THREE PLANES OF ANXIETY

Anxiety operates on three planes: body, mind and emotions (physiological, cognitive and psychological). The more severe the anxiety, the more these three planes will become distorted. Very often it is what is happening within the body that takes the person to the doctor. Figure 1 summarises the signs and symptoms of anxiety that can occur on each of the three planes.

If you checked three or more from each of the three lists in Figure 1, ask yourself:

1. How far does the fear of an anxiety attack limit your involvement in life?

2. How far are you going to avoid everyday situations?

3. How much of the time do you worry and feel tense?

How you answered the questions would influence whether you feel it advisable to seek help from your GP. A simple physical examination and talking over your feelings may be enough to reassure you that nothing serious is wrong. The GP may recommend light medication, or counselling which is likely to include teaching you how to relax.

Learning to relax is often the first step to controlling feelings of anxiety.

LEARNING TO COPE WITH ANXIETY

Coping is the means by which we avoid being harmed by life strains. Most people who work to alleviate the anxiety of others feel that the person has a better chance of coping successfully with the anxiety if encouragement is given to express and explore it. It is often a great relief to people to be given 'permission' to talk

BODY	MIND	EMOTIONS
Butterflies in stomach	I can't do it	Anger
Chest pains or other	What if I make a	Depersonalisation*
discomfort*	fool of myself?	Derealisation*
Dizziness, faintness,	People are looking	Depression
unsteadiness,	I could faint	Embarrassment
light-headedness*	It's a heart attack	Excessive worry
Dry mouth	Get me out of here	Fear of dying*
Fatigue	No on will help	Fear of going crazy
Hot flushes or chills*	I can't go alone	and doing
Feelings of warmth	I can't breathe	something
Heart palpitations*	I'm going to die	uncontrolled*
Hyperventilation	I'm going crazy	Feeling criticised by
Muscle tension/aches	I feel confused a lot	other people
Nausea*	I'm trapped	Feelings of
Numbness or	I'm not going out	doom/gloom
tingling, especially in	What if someone is	Isolated/lonely
the extremities*	hurt, sick, has an	Keyed up/on edge
Rapid, pounding	accident?	Panic
heartbeat	My thoughts are	Rejection
Shortness of breath,	speeded up	Terror
or a feeling of		Trapped – no way
smothering of		out
choking*		Unease
Sweating*		
Tightness of chest		
Trembling or		
shaking*		
Weakness all over		

The symptoms marked* are more severe in panic attacks though many may also be present in generalised anxiety.

Fig. 1.   Summary of the signs and symptoms of anxiety.

about their feelings. Factors which influence positive coping include the following.

1. Not thinking negatively about who you are and what you can do.

2. Supportive networks of family and friends may function to strengthen coping and, therefore, resistance by confirming self-worth in the face of challenges which tend to lower a person's resistance.

3. Problems arising at work are less likely to be successfully coped with than those that arise within the family. This is attributed to the impersonality of the workplace and the lack of intimate support.

4. There is no one way of coping that would ensure a person being able to ward off the stressful consequences of strains. It might be more realistic to talk of 'managing the strain', rather than 'change the strain'.

Coping with anxiety means taking control over your life.

Identifying four different ways of coping:

1. Find something positive in the experience. For example, if you joined a self-help group you might consider meeting other people as being a positive experience.

2. Use fantasy to create a preferred scenario. Imagine yourself in a relaxing situation, free from all tensions.

3. Search for information and advice. Adding to your awareness of what anxiety is often means that you find ways of coping with it. If you have access to the Internet, you could chat with people who have overcome anxiety.

4. Minimise the threat. Refuse to dwell on thoughts about whatever is causing the anxiety and make a conscious decision to put distressing thoughts aside. This might involve attending counselling to help you achieve some change in your thinking.

LEARNING NOT TO DEPLETE YOUR NERVOUS ENERGY

Nervous energy is not a barrel without a bottom. Every activity in which we engage uses a certain proportion of that energy. If we don't give ourselves time to recharge our inner batteries, we will cease to function effectively.

One of the most potent factors in keeping anxiety alive is fatigue. Many people live their lives constantly stretched like a bit of elastic, or like an over-wound clock spring. Such behaviour leaves us wide open to faulty eating, sleeplessness and breakdown of relationships. When we are at a low ebb we are particularly prone to anxiety attacks. None of us is entirely free of nervous tension all of the time. What matters is how we handle it. The following points may help you to handle your own nervous tension more effectively.

- Are you engaged in activities that constantly leave you with a feeling of low self-worth? If so, what can you do to change the circumstances?

- 'Live for today. The past is history, the future is a mystery, the now is a gift, that is why it is called the present.' (Source unknown.)

- Don't be driven by other people's unrealistic expectations of you.

- Don't be driven by always having to be perfect, nor beat yourself if you achieve less than 100 per cent.

- If you feel anxious, accept it, but don't play the invalid.

- Distinguish strictly between what is vital and what is un-important, and attend to the one and leave the other.

- Anxiety is often triggered by negative thoughts; make a ritual of creating a positive thought every day, and repeat it many times throughout the day.

CASE STUDY

Mark finds it hard to sleep

Mark, in his late 50s, says, 'I have terrible sleeping problems. There are times I wake up jumpy in the morning or in the middle of the night. I have trouble concentrating, even reading the news-paper or a book. Sometimes I feel a little light-headed. My heart races or pounds. I get keyed up before meeting clients and that makes me worry more.'

By itself, not being able to sleep is often a source of anxiety. So worry and disturbed sleep often create a vicious cycle. Mark's GP tries to assure him that there is nothing physically wrong. His blood pressure is within normal range, but he advises Mark to reduce his weight and cut down on his intake of coffee. Talking it through, Mark reveals being worried about his future. He no longer likes travelling around, but feels trapped where he is. Thus anticipating the future is one of the main focuses for learning to take control. As his sleep improves, so he becomes less anxious about his health and more able to contemplate continuing in the job for a few more years.

SUMMARY

- Nobody is entirely free from unwelcome situations or un-comfortable emotions; that is part of being human. But the lives of many people are so shaken by these feelings that they do not function as they want to. For them, anxiety has become a major problem.

- People who suffer from anxiety live constantly on the edge of suspense. They wait with dread for something unknown and fearful to attack them, yet often they cannot explain these feelings. If you feel wound up, as tight as a clock spring, give yourself daily times for refreshment and relaxation to recharge your batteries.

- Try not to feel ashamed that you feel anxious, for that will only increase your anxiety. Let other people help you, your GP or friends, for example. Take heart that you are not anxious every minute of the day. Try to stretch the times when you don't feel anxious. Enjoy the feeling and try to recreate it. Above all, try not to let events control your feelings.

2

Understanding the Body-Mind-Emotions Relationship

The body is probably the most wonderful machine ever created. It is so complex that we are still discovering things about it even after centuries of research. It is so constructed that all parts are designed to work in harmony, all relying on one another. The most complex computer is no match for what is contained in the human body. When one part is attacked, all other parts of the body cease to function properly. When this happens, the body is put under stress.

UNDERSTANDING THE BODY/BRAIN RELATIONSHIP

One vital part of the body is the brain. Much of what goes on within the brain is still a mystery, but we do understand the relationship between the brain and the rest of the body.

Figure 2 demonstrates the process, starting with a situation or an event. If a person flees or runs away, then the symptoms will clear up. If not, the chances are that distress will result, and the anxiety develop into an acute anxiety state. Changing the downward spiral rests on developing anxiety-reducing techniques, which may also involve medical intervention.

Understanding the nervous system

The nervous system, made up of the brain and spinal cord, and various sets of nerves, consists of two main parts – the **voluntary** and the **involuntary** or **autonomic**. See Figure 3.

MAKING SENSE OF THE BODY'S FIGHT/FLIGHT RESPONSE

The nerves of the autonomic nervous system activate the muscles of the blood vessels, the heart muscle and the smooth muscles of the digestive system. The autonomic nervous system is divided

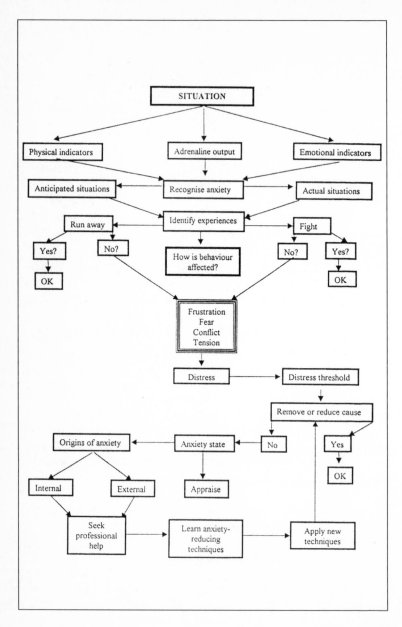

Fig. 2.   The A-Z of anxiety.

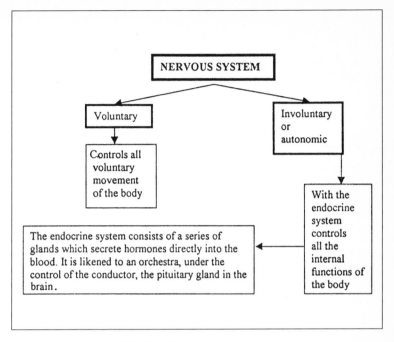

Fig. 3.   The nervous system.

into sympathetic nerves and parasympathetic nerves. Ordinarily, the two systems balance each other. If a sympathetic nerve triggers muscle contraction, for instance, a parasympathetic nerve orders muscle relaxation. The autonomic nervous system operates independently of voluntary control, although certain events, such as emotional stress, fear, sexual excitement and alterations in the sleep-wakefulness cycle, change the level of autonomic activity. These integrated responses maintain the normal internal environment of the body in an equilibrium state called **homeostasis**.

Knowing about the physiology

Certain voluntary activities activate the production of adrenaline from the supra-renal glands situated above the kidneys. Adrenaline (as well as other hormones) is necessary for the muscles to function – for example, to play that essential game of tennis, or complete the downhill ski run. This surge of adrenaline releases glucose into the blood to power the muscles. When the activity is done, the glucose is used up, and the heart rate returns to normal.

The fight/flight response is a primitive self-protection process. The effect of a stressful event is to mobilise the body's fight/flight system to combat a perceived enemy. Stress stimulates chemical, physical and psychological changes, to prepare the body to cope with a potentially life-threatening situation. The process is controlled by the autonomic nervous system and the endocrine system. The fight/flight process is:

1. The liver releases extra sugar to fuel the muscles.

2. Hormones are released that stimulate the conversion of fats and proteins to sugar.

3. The body's metabolism increases in preparation for increased activity.

4. Certain unessential activities, such as digestion, are slowed up.

5. Saliva and mucus dry up, so increasing the size of the air passages to the lungs and giving rise to the early sign of stress, a dry mouth.

6. Endorphins, the body's natural painkillers, are secreted.

7. The surface blood vessels constrict to reduce bleeding in case of injury.

8. The spleen releases more red blood cells to help carry oxygen, and the bone marrow produces more white cells to help fight infection.

Knowing whether to fight or run away

The autonomic nervous system, regulated by the **hypothalamus** (the stress centre), with the pituitary gland, is responsible for releasing more than thirty hormones that control these physiological responses to an emergency.

When neither response is appropriate – to fight or to run away – the biochemical changes have already been aroused and the body takes time to return to normal. It is the continued presence of the hormones that give rise to the prolongation of bodily symptoms described above. When appropriate action is taken, the chemicals are used up and the body returns to normal functioning.

> **People who experience anxiety live in a state of constant readiness to respond to fight or flight**.

A good example of the fight/flight response is when one cat suddenly comes upon another within its territory. Its back arches, its hair stands on end to make it look more menacing. Everything about the cat signals 'ready for action'.

Acknowledging physical symptoms

In Chapter 1 certain anxiety and stress-related symptoms were identified. Not every person suffering from anxiety experiences all of these, but there are certain symptoms which predominate in the catalogue presented by such people. Any of the major systems of the body can be affected – head, chest, heart, bowels, sexual organs, bladder, and muscles themselves.

One of the characteristics of anxiety is that the fear produced is every bit as tangible as if the person were facing a real situation. Most of us know what it feels like to be involved in a near-miss in a car, or some other accident; for the person suffering from anxiety, it is like that for much of the time, even though there is nothing real or actual to cause the sudden rise in fear. Often sufferers describe a horrible sensation in the pit of the stomach; such is fear, as if the whole stomach is about to drop out.

Finding appropriate help for symptoms

One of the things about anxiety is that the symptoms mimic definite diseases or illnesses, and so one of the great fears the person suffers from is that the racing heart indicates the onset of heart failure or a coronary; heartburn or diarrhoea herald cancer. Such fears are not to be confused with **hypochondriasis**, which is a morbid concern about one's health, especially when accompanied by delusions of physical disease. It is important to stress that the symptoms of anxiety result from an imbalance of the autonomic nervous system, and the pattern is continuous fear and tension which prolong the condition. However, it is also important not to fall into the trap of self-diagnosis. Rather a visit to the doctor to rule out illness than assume it is 'all in the mind'. That is dangerous.

UNDERSTANDING THE FEAR OF PALPITATIONS

It would be wrong to suggest that **palpitations** are the most serious of the fear symptoms of anxiety, but as the heart is such a vital organ, for on it depends so much, any involvement of the region of the heart naturally produces alarm. While it is certainly true that certain illnesses are accompanied by palpitations, discussion of these is beyond the remit of this book. What is important to remember is that palpitations are often related to anxiety. When they occur they in turn make the anxiety and fear worse, and so a vicious cycle is set up, where even the faintest tremor sets the fear racing. What happens in palpitations is a good illustration of the vicious cycle applied to most anxieties.

LEARNING TO RECOGNISE THE GREAT GIANT – FEAR

Maybe you recognise parts of yourself, or someone near to you, in the above descriptions of palpitations. If it is not palpitations, it might be the giant of the fear of cancer, where the focus is on the constant stomach irritation for which no physical cause can be found. Coupled with this is that the constant churning of the stomach often leads to loss of appetite, with weight loss, further adding to the fear.

It may be fear of a brain tumour where the focus is on head-aches. It may be the giant fear of sexual impotence. The ability to get an erection is very much under the control of the autonomic nervous system, and impotence is frequently the focus of anxiety for with it there is a threat to self-esteem (see Chapter 8). Under-lying all of these is the one word – *fear*. Other factors, such as guilt, shame, and disgrace, certainly contribute to the build up of anxiety, but often these are lost in swamping fear. Even sorrow over the death of a loved one is frequently infected by fear. The person whose work has become a burden, and who has to work increasingly longer hours to cope, is assailed by fear.

CASE STUDY

Sarah believes she is a failure

Many of us are caught up in reliving past fearful events, as if we were still trapped within them. Sarah was one such lady. 'I was brought up by a vindictive and controlling mother. I had little affection from either mum or dad. They sent me to boarding school when I was six.

'When I came for counselling I cried a great deal as I recalled how often I would be packed ready and waiting at the school front door to go home for the holidays, only to be told that my mother couldn't have me and I would have to spend the holidays at school.

'One of my mother's hateful remarks was, 'You're stupid.' I was so convinced that I *was* stupid that I grew up believing that I would never achieve anything. When I sat for my exams I failed them again and again, and left school with the minimum of certificates. Another failure! Whenever I entered the exam room I was overwhelmed by fear, and could scarcely breathe for the pounding of my heart.

'Part of counselling was to teach me relaxation, then, using imagery, to change my negative images of not passing into positive ones. Although I was referred the first time I sat my finals, I passed at the second attempt. This success started me on the road towards believing in myself. More than that, it gave me a valuable tool to help me take control of my life.'

LEARNING TO ADMIT TO FEAR

'Me afraid? Never!' Who of us really likes to admit to fear? Yes, we might admit to being afraid of spiders or, in my case, snakes, but what about imagined fears? Sarah's first task in counselling was to admit that she was afraid of failing, coupled with a fear that she would never come up to her mother's standards.

Your first step towards taking control
Perhaps your first step is to admit to your fear. But before you can do that, you have to identify what those fears are.

In Figure 2 fear is identified as being related to actual or anticipated events, in other words, real or imagined. Even where the situation is imagined, the fear can be just as powerful. Sarah learned to take control by using her imagination to create a positive scenario, even though the fear was based on reality. Sarah had become trapped in the vicious cycle of negative feelings, negative thoughts and fear. Overriding all of Sarah's fear was that she needed it. This might sound strange and unfeeling. But Sarah used the fear in two ways: to hang on to feelings of resentment against her mother and (unconsciously) as an excuse for her failures. Taking control meant that Sarah had to face up to changing her underlying motives; when she did that, she was able to move forward.

IDENTIFYING DISTRESS

Distress is anxiety turned up several notches. We can think of each of us having a stress tank, and unless appropriate outlets are provided the tank will overflow. The same applies in anxiety, where the anxiety turns into distress when the individual has become so fatigued, tortured and tormented by fear that no coping strategy has any effect. In other words, the continual inflow of fear has pushed the person over the top. In the model presented in this book, unless the cause can be removed or reduced, or effective coping strategies introduced, then professional help is most certainly indicated.

Taking control

It need not reach the stage of seeking professional help if the functioning of the body is fully understood, and *we* start to take control, rather than be controlled *by* fears which are often without foundation.

> **An essential part of the process is identifying what is causing the fear; what are the origins**.

A simple explanation, plus help from the GP by way of light sedation, plus counselling, might be all that is required to break the vicious cycle.

EXERCISE

Identifying what traps you in the past

1. List all the situations in which you know you still feel trapped. When you think about them you feel that knot in the stomach, or your breathing is affected, or you start to sweat.

2. Against every item state how you still feel trapped.

3. Arrange the list in order of degree of fear – 1 being low anxiety; 10 being high fear. This arranging of the list into a hierarchy is important, for you are already starting to exercise some control.

4. Start with the fear you graded as 1, and ask yourself these questions:
   - Why do I let this fear still rule me?
   - What do I gain from letting this fear rule me?
   - What would happen if I let this fear go?

5. Make a pact with yourself (written if necessary) that from today you will take control of one fear, by telling yourself that:
   - it is no longer appropriate
   - you refuse not to be in control of your life.

6. Take courage in both hands and tell someone else what you are doing. Remember, many people are frightened of telling others about their fears, lest the hearers think them silly and childish. This might be your first real test of courage.

SUMMARY

- Fear is an emotion produced by present or impending danger. The cause is apparent. Anxiety, on the other hand, is an emotion whose cause is vague or less understandable. Fear is a primitive emotion that can lead to the person either freezing, even to the stage of becoming mute, or fleeing. When neither fight nor flight is appropriate, the body takes time to return to normal, and this gives rise to feelings associated with fear. All organs of the body are vulnerable to attack by fear.

- Learning to admit to fear may be your first significant step towards taking control of your fear. The next step is to name your fears; doing so often weakens their hold. Many fears are without substance, being able to name the 'cause' helps you to realise that you have allowed a shadow to rule you. Shadows can frighten; they cannot kill, but the fear of them can.

3

Identifying Anxiety-Producing Situations

'A mortal, born of woman, few of days and full of trouble, comes up like a flower and withers, flees like a shadow and does not last.'
(Job 14:1. New Revised Standard Version)

Although Job does not talk of anxiety, trouble could be translated as anxiety. There is no guarantee that any of us will be exempt from anxiety, whether in mild or crippling form. There is no guarantee that the Welfare State, with its promise of care of the individual from the cradle to the grave, will save us from anxiety. Nothing anyone can do on our behalf can shield us from anxiety. All we can do is to accept that certain situations are liable to produce anxiety, and learn strategies to cope with those situations.

TAKING HEART

It could be easy to sink into depression, echoing Job's words that life is awful, but a few verses later he says;

'For there is hope for a tree, if it is cut down, that it will sprout again, and that its shoots will not cease. Though its root grows old in the earth, and its stump dies in the ground, yet at the scent of water it will bud and put forth branches like a young plant.'
(Job 14:7–9).

So in all your trouble, or anxiety, or whatever pulls you down, take heart. Don't spend your time looking down at the mud in which you shuffle; lift your eyes and see the trees, the birds and the sun. Sometimes the sun is hidden from view but it is always shining. You may feel that your anxiety is a gigantic cloud obscuring the warmth of the sun, but determine today that you will keep looking for the chink in the cloud that will allow the warmth to come through. Determine today that you will step off the tread-mill referred to in Chapter 1. No one can take you off, only you can do it. And you *can*. If you feel like Job, that you were destined to a life of anxiety, that nothing you can do can change that, then read the life of Job, and see how he hung on to his faith and eventually won through. If Job did it, so can you.

This chapter will be examining several specific situations which produce anxiety. Not everyone will relate to them all, but an understanding and awareness of the effects such situations create is one way to improve the ability to cope. Understanding might also help you understand other people's anxiety.

UNDERSTANDING PRE-NATAL ANXIETY

It has been suggested by various authorities that traumas which influence our later life can occur any time from conception to the first three years of life. That the baby in the womb responds to outside influences is well-documented. Noise, for example, is one outside influence to which the baby responds. If babies do respond while in the womb, then it is logical to assume that they also respond to emotions, as hormones are passed from mother to baby. Where there is disharmony between the parents, then how much of that is transmitted to the baby? If the mother is anxious, how much of that is transmitted?

Research on this is scant and conjectural. It could be argued that if a mother is anxious, then she is passing that on through example, after the baby is born, rather than while in the womb. What is important is not that the roots of the anxiety are traced to the womb (for that might lead to blame being attached to the mother) but that the person is helped to understand the nature of anxiety and how to cope with it.

UNDERSTANDING THE ANXIETY OF PUBERTY AND ADOLESCENCE

Puberty and adolescence, with their psychosexual development, are two epochs – or two parts of the same epoch – that most people would agree to be times of anxiety. The biological drive, which is pushing young people towards maturity, only serves to emphasise the constraints laid upon them, and often leads them into conflict with parents and others in authority whom they see as responsible for thwarting their desire for independence.

Intellectually they may accept that the constraints are reasonable, but emotionally they may not. This state of acceptance/non-acceptance leads to confusion, causing many young people to seek counselling to help them through this bewildering stage of their lives.

UNDERSTANDING SEPARATION ANXIETY

School is a time of anxiety. Most children cope with going to school without too many problems. For others, school is a place of torture, punishment and isolation, where every day heralds symbolic execution. For the parents, and more often the mother, school is what separates her from part of herself, her child. Sometimes the mother is so consumed with anxiety that she cannot rest until the end of the school day. It is as if she needs the child's constant presence to reassure her that she is still needed and is of some worth. If this sounds over the top, be assured that it is not, for it puts into words what many mothers feel.

Infants of about 7 to 10 months of age may experience what is called **stranger anxiety**, where they cry when approached by an unfamiliar person. A month or two later they may cry when their mother leaves them in an unfamiliar place; this phenomenon is called **separation anxiety**. There is dread of some unspecified danger, either from the outside or from mounting internal tension, which often results in inappropriate and excessive anxiety on being separated from the home environment such as when going to school.

How separation anxiety shows itself
Four common manifestations of separation anxiety are:

1. Unrealistic worries about harmful things happening to the attachment figure while away.

2. Persistent fears of being lost, kidnapped or even killed if separated.

3. Social withdrawal.

4. Refusal to sleep unless in the company of the major attachment figure. Sleep is often disturbed by nightmares about
   being separated from the significant person.

Mothers of children who suffer from separation anxiety very often
have a history of anxiety themselves. It seems that anxiety in the
mother, during the early life of the child, may disrupt mother-
child interaction and may create fertile ground for anxiety in the
child.

Home-sickness

This is a lesser form of separation-anxiety disorder, although the
feelings can be very powerful. It is thought that home-sickness
and separation anxiety show in children who are unsure of their
place within the family. The 'sickness' and anxiety are a desire to
return home to make certain that the family has not disintegrated.
The main thrust of treatment is the reduction of anxiety in both
child and parent(s).

UNDERSTANDING THE ANXIETY OF PREGNANCY AND BIRTH

Pregnancy is usually one of life's happy events, yet it rates fairly
high on the anxiety scale. The sickness and discomfort affecting
the woman is often felt by the man. Women have to accommodate
to a changing body-image, and some – those whose emotions are
tied to their bodies – may experience extreme disgust and anxiety
at the visible changes taking place.

Husbands who carry around with them an inner picture of their
wives as slim, supple and active, may find difficulty coming to
terms with the new image. These conflicts can be stressful, as may
the changes of mood that so often accompany pregnancy. If the
pregnancy goes according to plan, anxiety usually lessens, but
where there are complications, such as high blood pressure or
threatened miscarriage, the anxiety levels are likely to remain
high. In subsequent pregnancies memories of the first influence
the feelings, and anxiety may again ride high.

A further source of anxiety is, 'Is my baby normal?' Although
tests and scans do reveal abnormalities there is still the agonising
wait and then, if a handicap is detected, the couple are left with
making a choice.

Experiencing family stress

The stress of nine months, coupled with the physical and emotional stress of the birth, often sour what should be a happy event. The joy at the new member of the family is often muted by the subsequent anxiety, uncertainty and disturbed sleep. The marriage may be subjected to stress as both partners have to accommodate the third member. Thus a life event, although basically happy and exciting, has its own in-built anxiety factor.

Understanding the anxiety of miscarriage

Other anxieties connected with pregnancy are miscarriage, the very difficult pregnancy and those instances where the course of a particular disease is worsened by the pregnancy. The trauma of a miscarriage is not, as some uninformed people would argue, 'over as soon as it happens'. The biological trauma of a terminated pregnancy is quite profound and it may take the woman many months before her body adjusts to what has happened. It may take a great deal longer for her to adjust psychologically. Miscarriage has connotations of death rather than of life as with a full-term pregnancy.

UNDERSTANDING THE ANXIETY OF INFERTILITY

Of particular significance are those couples who suffer the trauma and anxiety of being told, after having a barrage of tests, that one of them is sterile. Many relationships never recover from this blow to womanhood or manhood. Many such women feel unfulfilled, while men who are sterile feel that they have not proved themselves as 'men.' While such feelings may seem illogical and difficult to understand, this sort of comment may not help:

> 'It's plain daft to allow yourself to become so obsessed with infertility that you let it come between you and all the good living there is to be done. To yearn hopelessly for what you can't have is to be like a baby crying for the moon. I have much sympathy with those who are disappointed but cope with the disappointment; very little with those who grizzle for the rest of their lives over it, or who allow themselves to become hard and bitter, or who seek pity for ever because they couldn't get everything they wanted.'
>
> (A written comment made by a well-known woman journalist.)

Repeated attempts by in vitro fertilisation (IVF), where the couple are driven by what often becomes an obsession to have a baby, are bedevilled by the anxiety experienced as each time of the month approaches, where they try yet again and so often do not succeed. When they do there is another anxiety: will the woman carry full-term? Many couples become so overwhelmed by anxiety that they are forced into a decision – to continue trying or to accept the fact that they will remain childless.

Getting help when needed

People whose emotions are deeply wounded know, intellectually, that they are behaving 'childishly' but seem unable to make themselves act like adults. Those who do 'act like adults' can manage without counselling help. Those who cannot, need it. They are the ones who, if their life history is accurately traced, will probably have experienced some psychological trauma at an earlier stage to which this new trauma has become attached. Some anxiety still haunts them.

The reactivated feelings from the past refuse to let go of the present hurt feelings. The double burden thus weighs them down. No amount of 'pull yourself together' will avail unless, and until, the person concerned has the opportunity to express the pain of the past and present. If people cannot do this they may well retreat behind the defences of resentment and bitterness. But these defences are usually brittle and liable to crumble under future traumatic events which in themselves may not seem to be earth-shattering, but whose cumulative effect may be. Counselling should aim at defusing this cumulative effect.

Identifying particular anxiety-producing experiences and situations

The following twenty-eight situations are only some of life's experiences and situations that may create anxiety.

- Trying to develop a self-identity, separate from my parents and significant others.

- Trying to balance the need for independence with need for support from adults.

- Discovering my own needs and interests.

- Developing a realistic self-assessment of my abilities.

- Balancing different needs within an intimate relationship.

- Making joint decisions about my lifestyle, family values, child-rearing.

- Endeavouring to overcome the insecurity of inexperience.

- Learning to get along with others in a work setting.

- Adjusting to the emotional demands of parenthood.

- Balancing intimate relationships with children's demands.

- Balancing professional and personal commitments.

- Dealing with feelings of failure of not reaching set goals.

- Feeling that there might not be another chance to make major changes in life.

- Dealing with mixed feelings towards adolescent children.

- Taking an honest appraisal of my ambitions.

- Resolving conflicts between work and personal life.

- Maintaining a relationship with spouse/partner, without the children.

- Coping with feelings of loss when children leave home.

- Coping with feelings of loss as parents age or die.

- Watching other people climb the ladder of success within work.

- Learning that experience based on wisdom is of equal importance as knowledge-based skills.

- As the work role declines, developing new interests and friendships.

- Helping adult children cope with their new family responsibilities.

- Realising that other people's welfare also affects me.

- Handling highly charged decisions without being emotionally destroyed.

- Facing the challenge of illness or death of loved ones.

- Coming to terms with my life choices.

- Finding new sources of satisfaction outside of work.

EXERCISE

Using imagery to transform anxiety into peace
Part of being able to take control of your life, to transform anxiety, is to spend time in recall. The best time to do this is when you are relaxed. If you find it difficult to relax, tell yourself that you are in control. No one controls your body or your mind.

Creating peace
Think of the word 'peace'. Imagine it written in large letters, in any colour that takes your fancy. Let your mind dwell on all that is associated with peace. Don't analyse, don't reject, don't fight. Let your mind go back to times when you felt peace; situations of harmony; certain flowers, or images that represent peace. You will find that your body responds to what is going on in your mind and spirit. If you find other images intruding, accept them for what they are and substitute an image of peace. Above all, don't struggle to create peace. You may find that it takes several sessions before you feel comfortable with this way of working.

Reinforcing the message
When you feel at peace, repeat (aloud if you can) 'Every day and in every way I am living more at peace'. Repeat this several times every day. Write the exhortation on little cards and stick them in various strategic places – on the hall table, on the mirror, in your diary – to remind yourself of your contract with yourself. Don't concentrate on anxiety; concentrate on the opposite – peace.

In a few paragraphs, record what has happened, and the specific steps that you will take during the next month to begin to advance your plan to transform anxiety.

Changing gradually
Keep in mind that you are a product of what you inherited and past experiences, all of which influence you as you are now. Tell yourself repeatedly you prefer a life of peace over a life filled with anxiety. Transforming one minute of every day into peace will have an accumulative effect, as if you are creating little islands

in the middle of some vast swamp. The more islands you can create, the less swamp there will be for you to fall into.

CASE STUDY

John and Mary decide against testing for Down's syndrome

Mary says: 'Three years after we married I became pregnant. We were overjoyed. The doctors advised me to have a scan and other tests.' You see, John has a sister with Down's syndrome.'

John says: 'We spent some anxious days and nights discussing the options. I knew the difficulties of having a child with learning difficulties. But we never imagined the degree of conflict we would experience. What if the tests proved positive? Could we go ahead with an abortion?'

Mary says: 'We are both passionately against abortion. The choice was to have the tests and then make up our minds, or not to have the tests and let nature take its course. We discussed things with the doctor, and decided not to have the tests. We coped by refusing to dwell on what might happen.'

John says: 'Mary sang a great deal, and felt that she was communicating with her baby. We were both happy. We attended several genetic counselling sessions, and did not allow the prospect of a Down's baby to destroy our happiness and harmony. Ben was born, healthy and well.'

SUMMARY

- Nothing anyone can do on our behalf can completely shield us from anxiety. All we can do is to accept that certain situations are liable to produce anxiety, and develop strategies to cope with those situations. From the cradle to the grave we are all subjected to experiences which have the potential for anxiety in them.

- There are no guaranteed strategies to ward off anxiety, but there is little doubt that creating a place of inner peace is something positive and constructive.

- One powerful way of coping with anxiety is by using imagination and relaxation to create peace. Throughout this book there is an emphasis on using relaxation. There is sufficient evidence that relaxation does reduce anxiety; and if it can reduce anxiety levels, then it is logical to propose that it can help to prevent anxiety. Being able to use deep relaxation involves being able to let go. Some people find letting go very difficult, for they need to be in control. If this applies to you, and you are prone to anxiety, then working on being able to let go in relaxation might prove a significant step forward in managing your anxiety. Now might be an appropriate time to refer to Chapter 12, for discussion on relaxation and imagination.

4

Understanding the Anxiety of Relationships

There are all sorts of relationships: negative, casual, passing, lasting and positive. There are people with whom we are expected to have relationships, like family; there are other people with whom we have no wish to have relationships, but are thrown together with them by force of circumstance, like that between schoolteacher and pupil, or manager and worker. This chapter aims to explore some of the anxieties that may be present in relationships. Even positive relationships are not free from anxiety. Positive relationships are built up from certain qualities; when these qualities cease to operate, the relationship is in danger of collapsing. Give and take is an essential for a relationship to flourish.

Identifying seventeen positive relationship qualities

1. Accepting.
2. Appreciating.
3. Being happy with.
4. Caring.
5. Concern.
6. Confidentiality.
7. Feeling for and with the other person.
8. Genuineness.
9. Interest.
10. Liking.
11. Prizing.
12. Regard for the other person's worth.
13. Respect.
14. Sharing.
15. Tolerating different views.
16. Valuing the other person's independence.
17. Warmth.

UNDERSTANDING HOW INTIMACY CONTRIBUTES TO ANXIETY

The relationship with one's spouse or partner, whether hetero-sexual or homosexual, obviously has a different quality to the relationship with a friend, however close. But for any relationship to flourish, there has to be give and take, or reciprocation. When this ceases, the relationship will flounder and eventually die. No relationship is free from tension, but if the qualities listed above are developed, the relationship will survive. Anxiety is created when tensions remain unresolved, and is likely to escalate when one person, or both people, begin to fear the threat of the relationship ending.

> 'Intimacy is like a harp. The music it produces comes from all its strings. Intimacy means discovering the particular harmony and melody that is enjoyed by the people involved. Sometimes the melodies will vary. Sometimes a minor key will be more appreciated than a major one.'
>
> (Source unknown.)

Identifying intimacy
Intimacy is:

- The process of revealing one's inner self to others.

- A relatively intense engagement not necessarily reliant on words.

- The stage of life in which the primary developmental task is to establish an emotionally close, trusting and sexual relationship with another person.

- A synonym for closeness, sexuality or marriage.

- The state of being closely familiar with another person, not necessarily of the opposite sex and not necessarily sexual.

- Generally regarded as an essential ingredient of a healthy and satisfying life.

- An essential component of human well-being, without which the person is likely to suffer tension and anxiety.

The deeper the intimacy, the more the couple find themselves becoming one. This alone creates anxiety with the potential loss of identity. Lack of intimate relationships leaves people feeling emotional loneliness. Some people shun intimate relationships because they feel they could not cope with the anxiety if the relationship ended.

EXAMINING HOW SELF-DISCLOSURE CONTRIBUTES TO ANXIETY

Self-disclosure is essential in the development of an intimate relationship. However, inappropriate disclosure hampers the development of such a relationship, mainly because it arouses anxiety. Implicit in developing relationships, and in maintaining them, is that self-disclosure by one partner places an obligation on the other to match the disclosure. Inappropriate disclosure, according to the length of time of the relationship, and its degree of intimacy, might warn the other person off, because he or she is not prepared to disclose. Disclosure implies trust that what is disclosed will not be repeated, but trust like that develops over time and cannot be rushed.

Self-disclosure and relationships

- Newly formed relationships can founder on the rocks of premature and inappropriate disclosure.

- Appropriate disclosure enhances relationships.

- Inappropriate disclosure – too much, too soon – can create anxiety.

- When one person discloses appropriately, and the other does not, this can contribute to the breakdown of the relationship.

Learning to be intimate

The absence of an intimate relationship, the inability to share emotions, to trust others or make a commitment to a stable, lasting relationship, is often a significant cause of mental and/or physical distress and anxiety.

> ## The capacity for intimacy fosters self-worth and a feeling of belonging.

The ability to be intimate has its origins in the early parent-child relationship, and the successful resolution of any parent-child power struggles. By implication, people who have been deprived of parental love and a family to act as a role model, such as children brought up in care, may have difficulty in establishing and maintaining intimate relationships.

In most people there is a deep hunger for intimacy which can only be found in a relationship of commitment. Sexual experiences are no substitute for intimacy, for the sexual act can be carried out without any feelings of love. When an intimate relationship eludes us, we enter into a state of anxiety, characterised by even more frantic efforts to form one, but the anxiety acts as a barrier.

EXAMINING HOW LONELINESS CONTRIBUTES TO ANXIETY

Loneliness is something we feel and relates to the degree of emotional contact we have with others. So being with a crowd of people does not mean that we stop feeling lonely.

- **Emotional loneliness** stems from the lack or absence of a close attachment. This form of loneliness results in intense and unpleasant feelings of anxiety and apprehension.

- **Social loneliness** stems from the absence of adequate or effective social networks. The feelings associated with this type of loneliness – boredom and exclusion – are not as intense as emotional loneliness.

It would appear that it is not the number of relationships which ward off loneliness, but the *depth* of the relationships we do have, in other words, intimacy. It also seems that loneliness is linked to low self-esteem, anxiety, depression, shyness, self-consciousness and the lack of social skills which help in forming new relationships.

EXAMINING HOW ISOLATION CONTRIBUTES TO ANXIETY

The fear of death and of isolation keep many people from entering relationships of intimacy. But some people doubt their own existence so much that they feel they exist only in the presence of another person. Many undergo a 'fusion' with others, so that 'I' becomes 'we', resulting in the safety of conformity. Compulsive sexuality is a common antidote to the terrifying prospect of isolation. The sexually compulsive person relates only to part of the other, not to the whole.

Learning to feel safe

The person who finds intimacy difficult may be so terrified of allowing other people into his or her inner world, that they keep people at a distance. For such a person just talking about feelings means coming out from behind the safety-barrier which he or she has erected to protect the vulnerable self, and the anxiety of that is what keeps them at a distance. With courage, that can change. As the vulnerable person begins to experience intimacy, so he or she is able to redraw the boundaries and gradually begin to feel safe with intimacy.

EXERCISE

Identifying your experiences of isolation

This exercise involves the use of imagery. Imagine you are on a luxury cruise, when the boat is hit by a tornado. You are washed up alone on an island. Try to imagine your feelings of isolation. Being able to get in touch with those feelings might resurrect the anxiety you felt about times in your life when you felt isolated, even though other people were around. For example, you might have moved from the country to the city; how did you feel? You might have been in hospital; though surrounded by people, were there periods of feeling alone? One way of identifying your loneliness is to make a log of your day's activities, and see how often (and under what circumstances) you felt the need to be with other people, or one particular person.

EXAMINING HOW THE WORKPLACE CAN CONTRIBUTE TO ANXIETY

Work is not just an activity that occupies a person for so many hours a day. It becomes integrated into our personality. Work influences who we are, and we influence the work we do. It satisfies many basic needs, and if the workplace does not satisfy those needs, or many of them, tension and anxiety are created. In work there is a give and take.

Identifying the anxieties of working

Can you remember your first day at school? Did you experience fear, heart fluttering as you walked through the school gates and watched mother or father as she or he slowly walked away, waving, into the distance? Entering work for the first time is a strange and exciting experience, sometimes fraught with tremendous anxiety, which has within it echoes of the first day at school. In fact, new experiences are often associated with that early event.

For some children, that first day is a traumatic experience which is etched on their memory as if by the most powerful acid. So whenever, as adults, they embark on a new experience, such as a different job, they again feel the anxiety and stress of that early event.

When we enter the workplace we experience a dramatic change in our self-identity, in some instances amounting to an identity crisis. We have to come to terms with a new idea of power, and the fact that as newcomers we probably have little power. Whatever our own goals might be, we have to fit them in with the collective goals which operate in the workplace. We need to feel accepted and liked, but we don't know the rules of intimacy and contact. How do we avoid being left out?

Identifying the benefits of working

Despite all the stresses associated with work, its benefits are enormous.

- Work provides a sense of belonging.

- Work can provide different points of view because it can bring us into conversation with men and women from other backgrounds, generations and businesses.

- The workplace can be a wonderful place for humour which would not normally be heard elsewhere.

- Work can provide resources. Our workmates often have ideas, information and know-how which we do not have, and vice versa.

- Work can provide listeners to our problems. Who understands our work frustrations and pleasures better than someone who is doing the same job? Who would be safer to talk to about family problems than someone who is not involved?

- Working can provide cushioning and escape-valves for anger. We can tear into our work, instead of into the adolescent son. Being able to argue for a proposal is more productive than arguing against one's spouse or partner.

- Working can provide sympathy. The understanding of work-mates is a unique source of support, and often means more than 'professionalised' support. The work group is wider than our family; not as impersonal as strangers; not as polite as neighbours.

- The work group can provide conversation and intellectual stimulation.

- In the workplace, our work is evaluated more objectively than it is in more intimate relationships.

- Working can provide a source of praise and reassurance. Promotions and salaries are tangible proof of performance and self-esteem.

Understanding the anxiety of severance from work

Severance from work, either as retirement or redundancy, may be one of the most traumatic and anxiety-provoking events in our life. For most of us, work is the one single item that has occupied our life. Even though we dream about retirement, when that time actually arrives we are left with a massive vacuum.

If work has meant self-respect, recognition, value and purpose, the loss of them can be devastating. For many of us our self-esteem is, or has been, centred on the work we do.

EVALUATING THE ANXIETY OF A RELATIONSHIP BREAK-UP

Anxiety and many other feelings apply equally to the ending of any intimate relationship. The cords which bind two people together, with the passing of time become tighter. Even when the 'fit' between two people starts to loosen, the severing of the relationship is not achieved without leaving deep scars. When a relationship in which two people invest much of themselves ends, it inevitably brings a period of grief. Many rush into other relationships in an attempt to fill the vacuum.

Unlike deaths, broken relationships have one major difference; the partner is still around! A death is final, nothing can alter it, but for the one whose close and intimate relationship has fractured, the loss experienced is one of confusion, feeling abandoned, and loss of self-worth and dignity.

The loss of 'what used to be' home, family and security is often compounded by feelings of responsibility and guilt for what has happened. There is a constant looking over one's shoulder to the past, and a refusal or inability to risk looking at what the future may hold.

Anger and bitterness, coupled with extreme anxiety and a dramatic drop in self-esteem, are feelings that are present in any broken relationship. The road to recovery may be very slow indeed, and painful, and may never be resolved satisfactorily. The break-up of a meaningful relationship can create so much anxiety that the person's very foundations are shaken.

Coping with a broken relationship

- Do not withdraw from life.

- Do not deny the way you feel.

- Do not back away from relationships.

- Do not put yourself down for feeling vulnerable.

- Do not be surprised at sudden physical problems, such as sleeplessness, loss of appetite, feelings of nausea. They are all associated with the feelings of loss.

- Do not dwell on the unfairness of it all.

- Do not base relationships entirely on trying to please.

- Do not rush into another relationship.

CASE STUDY

John overcomes his anxiety
Details:

- John, aged 34.

- Job, agricultural equipment salesman.

- John has been made redundant.

- Qualifications: Qualified teacher of agricultural sciences.

- Married to Joan, who works as a health centre administrator.

- Two daughters, Vanessa, aged 13 and Rachael, aged 11.

- Buying their own house which they built themselves.

- John tried for other jobs without success.

- A man with a strong sense of family, he sees himself as a failure.

- His initial anxiety increased until it overwhelmed him, he saw suicide as the only way out. Joan persuaded him to come for counselling.

'Through counselling I began to see more clearly some of the alternatives available to me. Together we worked out the follwing choices.

1. I could invest my redundancy money and live on the interest.
2. I could set up a contracting business on my own.
3. I could teach full-time at the local agricultural college.
4. I could emigrate to Canada where we have relatives.
5. I could become a house-husband and let Joan work.
6. I could go on the dole.

I decided to go for starting my own business and to go back to teaching part-time. My eight-point action plan was:

1. Discuss things thoroughly with the family.
2. Use some of the redundancy package to purchase equipment.
3. Put an advert in strategic places.
4. Contact the local agricultural colleges.
5. Draw up a list of potential customers to write to and to visit.
6. Get some headed stationery.
7. Draft an introductory letter to potential customers.
8. The time-scale I set myself was that within three months I would have written to at least one hundred potential customers, and been to visit at least 25 of them.

'Quite frankly I was scared stiff, but I was determined to make a go of this new venture. I learned to cope with my anxiety by creating a list of my strengths and weaknesses, and making an action plan that made the most of my strengths. Above all, I involved my family as partners in the decision-making.'

It is important to stress the action plan. Developing a precise and workable action plan was essential for John to have something specific to work to. The whole process involved John in making sense out of confusion. The eight-point plan gave John a logical framework to work to, a plan that he felt was workable.

SUMMARY

- A positive relationship is the meeting place of two people; a place where each brings something and takes something away. It is a place where needs are met. Not all relationships have the same degree of intensity or intimacy, and not everybody wants or needs what other people want. Relationships will flourish so long as needs are being met; they will start to die when the needs of one person cease to be met.

- Termination of working relationships can be one of the most traumatic of experiences, leaving the person feeling vulnerable and violated. When decisions have to be made they invariably lead to anxiety, but this anxiety can be reduced by careful planning and working to a structure. Don't make decisions from your weaknesses. Know your strengths and use them. Above all, don't neglect to include others in your decision-making, especially if the decision involves them.

5

Understanding Panic Attacks, Phobias and Obsessions

Anxiety as discussed in the previous four chapters is almost always due to over-sensitised nerves and the person is often able to live a normal life, if somewhat restricted at times. For people who suffer from **panic attacks, phobias** and **obsessions**, however, their anxiety is frequently crippling and disabling.

IDENTIFYING ACUTE ANXIETY STATES

Anxiety sufferers find themselves on a treadmill from which there seems no escape.

- Those suffering from panic seem pursued by a relentless executioner, who hounds them into fearful situations of night-marish quality.

- Suffering from phobias is like being trapped on a giant Ferris wheel where each revolution means new terror.

- The person who suffers from obsessions can never rest, never knows peace, can never relax. Rituals must be performed to keep some unknown fear at bay. The anxiety is that if they relax, or rest, the fear will catch up with them and destroy them, although they are not sure how.

There are no magical cures, and it would be erroneous and unethical to suggest that a self-help book could cure conditions which stretch psychiatrists to the limit. This does not mean, however, that people who do suffer from these heart-rending conditions are beyond help, or even beyond self-help. Somewhere along the line there has to be a match between what the 'professional' is offering and the will of the sufferer. If this book helps one person to harness his or her inner resources just one little bit, and so feel more able to cope with whatever it is that bugs him or her, then it has to be good and positive.

People who suffer from any of the acute anxiety states discussed in this book do not need to be reminded of what it feels like; for them it is reality. But for other people what is discussed will hopefully help to bring some enlightenment. Here we need to distinguish anxiety in its simple form from what we are discussing in this chapter. The three conditions here – panic, phobias and obsessions – are so deeply embedded in the psyche that often very expert help is required.

UNDERSTANDING PANIC ATTACKS

The panic attack – the sudden, overpowering feeling of terror – is experienced by many people at some time in their lives. A panic attack typically lasts for several minutes and is one of the most distressing conditions that a person can experience. Many of the symptoms of acute anxiety are present in panic attacks.

Symptoms of panic accompany certain medical conditions of thyroid, the inner ear, epilepsy, intoxication and substance withdrawal, and cardiac conditions such as irregular heart rhythms or chest pains. People who suffer from **post-traumatic stress disorder** (see Chapter 9) may experience panic when they are faced with situations – even on the television – which resemble the original traumatic event. It is vital to receive a thorough medical check-up, and not take for granted that the symptoms are purely 'all in the mind'.

CASE STUDY

John describes his panic attacks

John, a painter and decorator, says, 'It begins in my gut, just a twinge at first, but then it quickly spreads out towards my heart and head. Then it floods through my torso, neck and brain like black dye through water, it colours my sanity with a dark foreboding and my confidence is swept away in its path. My heart, which reared up at first, seems to race faster and faster above a stomach made nauseous with its motion. I try to give the feelings words but my throat is dry and won't allow them to come. What voice does come is small and far away. And my breath, though quick, seems insufficient to fill my lungs. My face feels clammy and my thoughts are of one thing only, "Get away until all this ends." I feel demoralised, discouraged, ashamed and desperately unhappy because I can't carry out normal activities. Some people tell me I lack "moral fibre", and that hurts. It invades all other aspects of my life and other people get sucked into it.'

UNDERSTANDING PHOBIAS

A phobia is an extreme, irrational fear of a specific object or situation, and the anxiety may vary in severity from unease to terror. A phobic disorder interferes with a person's ability to work, to socialise and go about a daily routine. A phobia that interferes with daily living can create extreme disability and the person needs medical treatment.

Phobias occur when fear produced by an original threatening situation is transferred to other similar situations, with the original fear often repressed or forgotten. All forms of phobias are disabling conditions, and even mild forms can create problems in daily living. Phobias are associated with high incidence of distressing thoughts about suicide. Fear of blood and injections may mean that the person avoids essential and urgent medical or dental care. Phobias generally respond to anti-depressants and to behavioural forms of therapy. For example, **cognitive restructuring therapy** seeks to replace faulty thinking patterns with more constructive ones. The client says, 'I'm a complete failure'. The therapist then challenges this by getting the client to state in which areas of life he or she is successful. It is highly doubtful that someone is hopeless in everything.

Understanding simple (specific) phobias
A simple phobia is of a specific object, animal or situation. Irrational fears of snakes, heights, enclosed places and darkness are examples. Receiving an injection or seeing blood may also assume phobic proportions. Some common phobias are fear of:

- mice or small animals (zoophobia)

- spiders (arachnophobia)

- height (acrophobia)

- open spaces (agoraphobia)

- enclosed spaces (claustrophobia).

In fact, almost anything can be the focus of a phobia. One medical textbook lists thirty-three specific situations. Phobias are quite resistant to change without treatment, although **desensitisation therapy** has proved effective. In desensitisation the person is exposed, under relaxed conditions, to a series of stimuli that gradually come closer to the anxiety-provoking one, until the stimuli no longer produce anxiety.

Understanding agoraphobia
People with agoraphobia avoid open spaces, crowds and travelling. Agoraphobia, which literally means 'fear of the marketplace' and indicates fear of being away from the safety of home, commonly occurs with panic disorder. Where escape is impossible the feelings of anxiety are endured with marked distress.

Understanding social phobia
Social phobia is the irrational fear and avoidance of being in a situation in which a person's anxieties could be watched. Fear of public speaking, or of eating in public, are the most common complaints of socially phobic individuals. Social phobia sufferers are invariably loners and lonely and often fail to develop intimate relationships. Social phobias are often associated with alcohol abuse.

In children the fear may take the form of tantrums, screaming, freezing, clinging or refusing to move away from a familiar person. Young children may be excessively timid, refuse to make contact with other children in play, are often seen on the fringes of a group and prefer to stay close to familiar adult figures.

CASE STUDY

Jenny is terrified of flying
Speaking of the fear of flying, Jenny says, 'I'm scared to death of flying, and I never do it any more. When that aeroplane door closes I feel trapped. My heart pounds and I sweat buckets. If somebody starts talking to me, I get very stiff and preoccupied. When the plane starts its take-off it just reinforces that feeling

that I can't get out. I picture myself losing control, freaking out, climbing the walls, but of course I never do. I'm not afraid of crashing or hitting turbulence. It's just that feeling of being trapped. Whenever I've thought about changing jobs, I've had to think, "Being a stewardess is not a job I'll be looking at." These days I only go places where I can drive or take a train. My friends always point out that I couldn't get off a train travelling at high speeds either, so why don't trains bother me? I just tell them it isn't a rational fear.'

UNDERSTANDING OBSESSIONS

Obsessions are recurring or persistent thoughts, ruminations, images or impulses which seem to invade a person's consciousness despite all attempts to ignore, suppress or control them. Obsessional thoughts are frequently morbid, shameful, repugnant or merely tedious; they are usually experienced as being meaningless and are accompanied by anxiety to a varying degree.

People with the life-wrecking obsessions and rituals of **obsessional compulsive disorder (OCD)** should not be confused with a much larger group of individuals who are sometimes called 'compulsive.' These people hold themselves to a high standard of performance and are perfectionists and very organised in their work and even in recreational activities.

OCD sufferers often attempt to hide their disorder rather than seek help. An unfortunate consequence of this secrecy is that people with OCD usually do not receive professional help early enough. By the time they do they may have learned to work their lives – and family members' lives – around the rituals. Stress is known to make OCD worse.

The following situations provide examples of obsessive compulsive disorder.

- A man will not go to public places because he fears he will have intolerable sexual thoughts or falsely accuse someone of committing a crime.

- A woman plugs and unplugs electrical appliances twenty times or more, counts her change ten times whenever she shops, and habitually stares at the addresses on envelopes for several minutes to make sure they are correct.

- A man's persistent urge to shout out an obscenity or blasphemy in church can be suppressed only by counting slowly backward from 100 to one.

- A man feels a drop in his eye as he looks up while passing a building and cannot dismiss the thought that someone with AIDS has spat out of a window. To reassure himself, he proceeds to knock on the door of every office in the ten-storey building.

- A man covers everything he touches with a paper towel first. If he happens to touch a bed-frame or a bathroom door handle with his hand or part of his clothing, he must wash the contaminated object immediately. He will not let his left hand touch anything at all.

- For five years a woman has been washing her hands up to the elbow thirty to sixty times a day until they are raw and scabbed, 'to prevent my family from being infected'. She constantly calls her vicar to ask him whether her thoughts and actions are morally correct.

- A young woman has dropped out of college and spends all day at home, often in darkness with her eyes closed, trying to shut out violent and sexual thoughts and images.

- A young woman washes her hair three times as opposed to once because three is a good luck number and one isn't.

- A man is always worried that if he doesn't do something, his parents are going to die.

- A woman can't write the word 'death' because she is worried that something bad will happen to her or someone she loves.

IDENTIFYING PREFERRED MODES OF TREATMENT

Behaviour therapy, which makes heavy demands on the person, is probably the most successful treatment, but that road is not an easy one for the client to tread. John, with an obsessional fear of contamination, was treated by exposure, being taught to 'soil' his hands with dirt and then to avoid washing them for longer and longer periods. **Anxiety-management** training enables John to withstand the anxiety he feels during the period of exposure. This is where the person is exposed to various carefully graded situations which build up confidence. When the person copes with the anxiety of one situation, the next one is tackled, until the most feared situation is tackled.

Homework and tasks are set. The behaviour therapist will constantly challenge what John says, so bringing various parts of John's statement or behaviour into focus. Generalisations are turned into specifics, and excuses and rationalisations are disputed. At the same time, the therapist offers a great deal of support as John handles (to him) terrifying situations and attempts to stop doing something. The support offered by the therapist could be staying with John while he carries out the feared task, giving practical advice like, 'take some deep breaths', 'focus on becoming relaxed', 'imagine yourself doing it'. The aim of support is to give John the skills to use when he is on his own.

CASE STUDY

Neil experiences the benefits of behaviour therapy

Neil says, 'It is terrifying for me, because my fear is going into a pub for a meal. Unless I wash every vegetable twenty times they will not be clean, and if they are not clean then something dreadful (though I don't know what) will happen, and I can't be sure that the vegetables in the pub will be clean. The task the therapist gave me is to walk in and sit down and order, and then stay to eat the meal. I didn't achieve all this in one go, mind you, but little by little I did it. I rehearsed what I had to do in the safety of the session. The therapist taught me progressive relaxation and helped me use imagery, before trying it for real. The first time I was petrified, so the therapist came with me, and supported and guided me. He said, "Take a deep breath and let it out slowly." "Your fists are clenched, relax them." "Tell yourself you can do it." I couldn't have done it on my own.'

SUMMARY

- Panic attacks, phobias and obsessions are all characterised by incapacitating and exhausting terror. Certain medical conditions can present symptoms of panic, for example dysfunctions of the thyroid gland, disturbance of the balancing system of the inner ear and disturbances of the heart rhythm. Even too much intake of caffeine can mimic anxiety. However, it should not be taken for granted that it is 'all in the mind', for such conditions warrant medical intervention.

- Behaviour therapy, with supportive counselling and medication, is the preferred combination of treatment for panic, phobias and obsessions. Behaviour therapy focuses on modifying observable behaviour and thoughts that relate to behaviour.

- Although the road towards being free from phobias and obsessions is long and often disheartening, many people have overcome these crippling conditions. In learning to conquer any of the anxiety states, there has to be a partnership between sufferer and therapist. The therapist can only do so much; the sufferer is the one who is motivated to recover.

6

Learning to Conquer Guilt, Shame and Disgrace

The trinity of **guilt, shame** and **disgrace** feed on one another and create uncontrollable anxiety. Guilt and shame are both characterised by self-reproach; the feelings of disgrace are linked with some action which is perceived to be shameful. In the view of Aristotle anger is caused by undeserved slight, fear (anxiety) by the perception of danger, and shame by deeds that bring disgrace or dishonour.

Sociologists consider guilt and shame to be mechanisms of social control. From a theological perspective, guilt is a fact or state attributed to a person who violates the will of God and/or some moral or penal code. The focus of guilt is on specific blameworthy actions that one has performed, whereas shame is focused on the inadequacy of the entire self. Guilt is when we fail to reach the standards of society; shame is when we fail to reach our own standards. On this account, the negative evaluation of shame is more global and painful than that of guilt.

The *Oxford English Dictionary* defines disgrace as:

> *disfavour of one in a powerful or exalted position, with the withdrawal of honour, degradation, dishonour which accompanies it.*

What is important about this last definition is that the disgrace need not relate to someone who has 'fallen from grace', by having committed some crime that has brought dishonour; people can feel disgrace over some quirk of nature, such as disfigurement.

UNDERSTANDING GUILT

As we grow up we internalise certain standards and values – this is a part of being socialised. We may also develop the capacity to punish ourselves for our own misdeeds by feeling badly about ourselves and otherwise making ourselves feel varying degrees of misery.

> **Guilt is awareness of having violated personal norms, or the norms of family, religion or society. The offence may be real or imaginary**.

Normally the reason for the guilt is known only to the person concerned. The feeling of guilt may or may not be proportional to the nature of the offence. Guilt is often experienced as an alienation from relationships with God, others, or self.

Guilt may provide a sense of being able to rectify the situation; it may motivate a person to make restitution. It may, therefore, encourage empathy and behaviour that benefits other people. However, where restitution is not possible the guilt cannot go away and anxiety is created.

Understanding 'false guilt'

For many people, understanding the mechanisms of guilt often brings immediate relief. Perhaps this is nowhere seen more clearly than in what is called **false guilt**. It is likely to be associated with thoughts and feelings connected with sexuality, self-love and putting oneself first, often called being selfish which does nothing to relieve guilty feelings.

A distinction needs to be made about *having* desires to do 'wrong' and *acting* upon such desires. People who live their life according to some highly moral standard are often the ones most troubled by such thoughts. It is possible that such people are pursued by religious teaching that 'everyone who looks at a woman with lust has already committed adultery with her in his heart' (Matt. 5:28, RSV). Guilt about having 'wrong' desires often wreaks havoc on the psyche, producing severe breakdown. False guilt can be very anxiety-provoking, possibly because we feel unable to exercise any control over what is causing the guilt. It can be very self-destructive.

Taking control

It is paradoxical, but the more we struggle against such thoughts, the more they will come and the stronger they will be. An old Chinese proverb says, 'You can't stop the birds flying over your head, but you can prevent them nesting in your hair.' Thoughts come unbidden, and one way to deal with them is to say, 'Ah! Here is that thought again. It will go presently and I don't need to do anything about it.' 'Naughty' thoughts should be treated like migrant birds – let them pass over; don't give them house room. This simple strategy helps you to exercise control.

Finally, be aware that guilt is telling us something. Acknowledge it. Do something about it if you can. Don't engage in laying blame, but seek to understand that guilt exists in the gap between what we would like to be and what we are. A great part of what we would like to be results from many influences thrust upon us at an age when we were easily moulded, like Plasticine. We may need to do a great deal of heart-searching to discover where the roots of our guilt arise.

Understanding guilt and self-blame

Blame is anger directed outwards at someone else. But blame may also be self-blame, whereby the person internalises the feelings of responsibility. Self-blame is detected in such sentences as, 'I should have known better.' 'Idiot!' 'I never get things right.' Such discounting language has a damaging effect on self-esteem.

> **Blame is linked with guilt, and guilt may be anger turned inwards**.

Many people spend much of their life accepting blame for what goes wrong, and feeling guilty over what is clearly not their fault. Some are caught up in chronic self-blame when they are the innocent victims of, for example, crimes committed by parents, or the relatives of someone who has committed suicide, or the survivors of some horrific accident. On a wider front, self-blame is often felt by people whose nation has fallen into disgrace over atrocities.

LEARNING WHAT YOU CAN DO TO CONTROL GUILT

- Make amends when you can. Amends may be symbolic. Write a letter or make a tape in which you put things right.

- Learn from your mistakes.

- Identify what your 'guilt buttons' are and which people keep pushing them.

- Drive away ghosts. Old memories are often triggered off by current events.

- Live for today and count your blessings.

- Don't condemn yourself because of thoughts you consider to be bad.

- Don't have sexual relationships that damage your self-esteem, or hurt other people.

- Let love, not hate, direct your energies in sex, and so far as possible in other activities.

- Try to avoid doing things that your conscience warns you against.

- Try not to let your conscience tyrannise you into not being able to enjoy yourself, being driven to overwork and puritanical attitudes. Not being able to enjoy sexual pleasure is often a manifestation of a tyrannical conscience.

- Work to forgive yourself. Forgiveness is an act of will. Wait for it to happen and it never will.

UNDERSTANDING SHAME

Shame is a complex, painful feeling resulting from a strong sense of guilt, unworthiness or disgrace.

> **We feel shame when we are faced with something that draws attention to a discrepancy between what we are and what our ideal self would like to be**.

The act that causes shame is often inconsequential, but the self feels attacked. Shame is focused inward, producing a sense of helplessness, a fear of others' disapproval and a desire to hide from situations involving other people. These symptoms may motivate the shamed person to blame others and become angry.

Shame is a punishment imposed from without – for example, when members of a group or community publicly ridicule, scold or ostracise someone for misbehaving. This kind of punishment can be extended to relatives of the offender, which causes them to feel a strong investment in controlling the behaviour of family members.

Like its kindred state, guilt, shame may arise in connection with matters of sex, but it is also found in a great variety of situations not concerned with sex. The sense of shame consists in the consciousness of failure and exposure before other persons in connection with a point of honour or of strong self-esteem.

Blushing is often an expression of shame, and is frequently accompanied by other signs, such as the drooping of the body, lowering of the head and averting the gaze. We tend to hide or want to hide, to escape notice and, in extreme cases, to inflict injury upon ourselves as a kind of self-imposed punishment for some imagined wrong committed.

Getting to the root of shame

Shame may also arise from a conflict between impulses, or from comparison with someone to whom we consider ourselves inferior in some way. We then act in a way that draws attention to the powers and attributes in which we consider ourselves deficient. So the self-fulfilling prophecy is completed.

Some sociologists speak of **shame cultures**: eg the traditional Japanese culture, and **guilt cultures**: eg Judaeo-Christian cultures.

Jung makes a distinction between **collective guilt** and **personal guilt**; a sense of guilt may arise from either. Collective guilt may be compared to fate, or to a curse, or to a form of pollution. An example of collective guilt would be where a nation feels guilty about the crimes of a previous generation, such as the Holocaust.

MAKING THE CONNECTION BETWEEN GUILT, SHAME, DISGRACE AND ANXIETY

All three states create anxiety because what they have in common is fear. Whereas anxiety centres on some anticipated event or situation, guilt, shame and disgrace are usually linked with some actual event. However the feelings, which might have been normal and acceptable, border on being abnormal because they continue long after the event.

It would seem that the anxiety of guilt, shame and disgrace are linked to other people's disapproval and censure. Where the event or situation is in the public domain, people's attitudes influence just how long the person's feelings are kept alive. Where something is kept secret, there is the constant anxiety that 'it' will be discovered and made public.

> **People who suffer from guilt, shame or disgrace are often not able to forgive themselves, even though they might be ready and willing to forgive other people**.

This constant state of unforgiveness keeps the fires of anxiety burning brightly, and the person lives on the edge of some dreaded punishment.

CASE STUDY

Betty is intolerably guilty

'I have been troubled by guilt for over forty years, since our daughter, Catherine, was born with Down's syndrome. Over the years the guilt has led to periods of deep sorrow, extreme guilt and the feelings of disgrace at having brought a handicapped child into the world. No amount of 'reasoning' has helped me; no logical explanation that I was not to blame has helped to assuage my feelings.'

(In Betty's case the feelings of guilt, shame and disgrace were almost delusional.[1] An example of a delusion would be that I believe that I am the rightful heir to the British throne, even though my family history does not support this.)

'I know, logically, that there is no reason for feeling as I do. Catherine's birth was an accident of nature. I had not 'done' anything to bring this about. There had been no sin of omission or of commission.'

Some people feel guilt because they have done something, or not done something. A case was reported in the newspapers recently where a man walked into a police station twenty years after he had been involved in a hit and run, and the pedestrian

---

[1]A delusion is a persistent false belief which is both untrue and that cannot be shaken by reason or contradictory evidence, and which is inconsistent with the person's knowledge or culture.

had died. The driver had not been able to live with the guilt any longer, and made the only reparation he knew – confession.

Betty feels she is a disgrace

We saw that Betty felt a sense of disgrace for having given birth to a not-perfect child, and this sense of imagined public disapproval remained with her. Added to this was the prejudice she had to cope with. Betty said, 'When I took Catherine out, people would come over to look in the pram then hastily turn away. I could see the embarrassment in their eyes, and it hurt. I wanted to shout at them, 'I haven't done anything wrong, and neither has she,' but somehow I felt that would be a lie; that I had done something wrong. It wasn't made easier when some religious people knocked at the door, and when they saw Catherine they said, 'Somebody must have sinned for that to happen.' How could people be so bigoted? It certainly made me feel angry and bad at the same time. I felt I had brough disgrace on the whole human race, and certainly to my family. I think I've passed this on to the other children.'

There was little that I, as counsellor, could do, but listen and try to understand Betty's deep feelings of total responsibility. There was no good in my saying, 'It will pass,' for something within me told me that it wouldn't. At one stage Betty said, 'It's not like a prison sentence that has an end to it. Then I could plan; the guilt and disgrace are like a life-sentence that goes on unremittingly.'

Disgrace may be assuaged by forgiving the person who has committed some act, but Betty could find no one to blame, except herself. But Betty did not allow herself to wallow in self-pity, for her experience increased her feelings of compassion toward other people, and particularly toward children in need.

Sam rises above his disgrace

If you hve committed some act that has brought you into disgrace, you have two choices: to buckle under it, or rise above it. Sam was one such person. 'I disgraced myself and my family when I was accused and convicted of abusing children. My three years in prison was a time of reflection and reappraisal.

While in prison I studied psychology and counselling, gaining an Open University degree. On my release, although I knew I could never work with children, I began working for a counselling organisation.

I made no secret of my past, and was encouraged by the support

I received from my family and then from my new colleagues. One of them summed it up when she said to me, "If we can't learn to forgive; if we can't encourage someone to try again, what use are we as counsellors." I've made that my motto.'

SUMMARY

- In Freudian terms, guilt arises from the conflict between basic desires and what the super-ego (the conscience) dictates. Furthermore, in the relationship to anxiety, guilt is related to something in the past, while anxiety is related to some feared occurrence. Shame, on the other hand, is thought to arise from fear of ridicule, or a failure to live up to one's self-ideal.

- Both guilt and shame generate anxiety. The first step to controlling guilt and shame is to admit to them. Then make amends if you can. If you can't make a symbolic reparation, then try to substitute positive for negative thinking. Some people might find relief by confessing to a priest, if there is a definite action which is causing the guilt.

- Feeling shame over something over which you have no control equates to false guilt. False guilt and shame would probably be more appropriately dealt with by a counsellor than a priest. However, where shame arises from 'wrong' or 'unclean' thoughts, a priest might be more helpful than a counsellor.

- Feeling guilty might be your way of punishing yourself. You may be taking your anger out on yourself, because it is safer to do that than be angry with someone else. Being honest with yourself could be an important step in getting rid of guilty feelings.

7

Understanding the Anxiety of Eating Disorders

This chapter discusses two eating disorders – **anorexia nervosa** and **bulimia nervosa**. The link with anxiety is that many people with eating disorders also experience social phobias, for example feeling humiliated or embarrassed to be seen eating in public, or obsessive compulsive disorders related to food.

Eating disorders such as anorexia nervosa and bulimia arise predominantly (though not exclusively) in young women. There is an increasing incidence of young men who are becoming anorexic.

An excessive concern with body image and a morbid fear of becoming fat are hallmarks of these conditions. Anorexia nervosa is the opposite of obesity. It seems to occur only in societies where adequate food is taken for granted and where people may feel anxiety about avoiding obesity. The physical effects of a young woman starving herself down to 90 pounds (45 kilograms) or less differ in several ways from those of famine. The young woman with anorexia nervosa usually eats inadequate protein and essential nutrients; she is restless and overactive, often in sports and keep fit.

Research has shown that the risk of anorexia nervosa may be six times higher for people who have immediate relatives with the condition.

UNDERSTANDING ANOREXIA NERVOSA

Anorexia nervosa is refusal to eat, or an abnormality in eating pattern, not a loss of appetite. It occurs most commonly among adolescents but is also observed in older people. It is commonly referred to as a 'female' problem, although it is not an exclusively female condition. The starvation regime may be pursued relent-lessly, resulting in death. It was named about a hundred years ago, exists in many countries of the world and occurs in about one in a hundred females between 16 to 18 years. The value and attractiveness of being slim are communicated via the media and respected adults.

Identifying the principal symptoms of anorexia

- The person's aim is to produce marked weight loss.

- A morbid fear of becoming fat.

- Evidence of amenorrhoea (cessation of menstruation) in women, and loss of sexual potency and interest in men. (A woman is considered to have amenorrhoea if her periods occur only following hormone administration.)

- Refusal to maintain body weight, consistent with normal weight for age and height.

- Intense fear of gaining weight even though obviously under-weight.

- Avoids food, indulges in purging, self-induced vomiting and vigorous exercise.

- Severe electrolyte disturbances which can result in death. (Electrolytes are substances in the body that play an essential role in the working of the cells, and in maintaining fluid balance and a normal acid-base balance.)

- Low self-esteem.

- A tremendous need to control their surroundings.

- Anxiety and unhappiness, irritability and depression.

- A neurotic preoccupation with reducing weight.

- Often a history of relationship difficulties, and fear of meeting strangers.

- Extreme weight loss over prolonged periods results in impaired reasoning and logic.

UNDERSTANDING BULIMIA NERVOSA (BINGE-EATING)

Bulimia is marked by binge eating followed by acts of purging (eg self-induced vomiting, swallowing of laxatives, or diuretics which result in water loss rather than loss in calories, or vigorous exercising) to avoid weight gain.

Bulimia, as in anorexia, is a morbid fear of becoming fat. It may occur in someone who has previously been anorexic, or following substance abuse. Self-loathing and disgust with the body are even greater than in anorexia nervosa.

Identifying important points about bulimia

- The excessive eating, which causes distress, is not within the person's control.

- Binges may be triggered by anxiety, depression or loneliness.

- People who have also experienced anorexia are more prone to develop bulimia. This is thought to be when the iron-like control over not eating suddenly cracks and results in a binge. Guilt takes over resulting in self-induced vomiting. The starvation and binge cycle starts all over again. Guilt is not always present; some people say that binging soothes feelings of stress and anxiety.

- Bulimia may start just as the anorexic person is reaching optimum body weight.

- Bulimia follows a period of self-imposed starvation. The body revolts against this deprivation and the food gorged is what the body most needs, especially carbohydrates.

- During the binge episode (which may last just minutes or hours) people often describe a sense of frenzy.

- Pressure may push the recovering anorexic into bulimia.

- Not all bulimics have been anorexic, but they are just as fearful of putting on weight.

- Bulimics are thrown into panic when they feel that their body has taken control away from them.

- Bulimics fear that if they start eating they will devour everything in sight.

- The mind of the bulimic is constantly full of thoughts about food. They dream about it. This is similar to the experiences of POWs in concentration camps, whose daydreams were often about food.

- Binge eating is usually done in secret, and the buying of the food is so arranged that no one could be suspicious.

- Sustained use of stimulants often brings depression in its wake. Deterioration of relationships is also a factor in this depression.

- Constant vomiting is harmful because the body is deprived, not only of food, but of gastro-intestinal juices essential for health. Juices that have their function in the stomach, have a harmful effect on the upper parts of the alimentary tract. Continual loss of fluid often leads to dehydration.

- Many bulimics overspend and get into financial difficulty. So overpowering is the desire for food that some will steal to get it.

- Few bulimics succeed in a long-term, lasting sexual relation ship.

- Most bulimics, male and female, have a low self-esteem and desperately seek approval.

- The basic conflict is their need to be admired and desired by a member of the opposite sex on the one hand, and a fear that they are not good enough and will be rejected, on the other.

- Unlike anorexics, bulimics normally continue to menstruate. Some conceive and a few give birth. Many, however, are against the idea of becoming pregnant.

- Because bulimics normally weigh more than anorexics, their eating habits may escape notice for years.

- When bulimics have successfully controlled binging for a period they generally feel afraid when they feel the desire coming on.

- Shame and secrecy associated with the disorder often result in social isolation, and impaired functioning at work.

- Bulimics are more motivated to seek help and be rid of the condition than anorexics.

UNDERSTANDING COMPULSIVE EATING

Compulsive eating, which typically results in obesity, is where eaters feel compelled to eat for an assortment of reasons in addition to, but not limited to, real physical hunger. These people become overweight when they eat more food than their bodies need, and/or they consistently choose the wrong kinds of food (high fat/high calorie/high sugar). People who compulsively eat may be very distressed about their food intake and body size or they may seem not to care at all. Some are amazingly unaware of the fact that they have a problem.

Eating disorder has a cost, negatively affecting such areas of life as physical health, mental/emotional health, spiritual life, relationships, school/job performance.

UNDERSTANDING THE ESSENTIALS OF TREATMENT FOR EATING DISORDERS

- Hospital admission may be necessary, to restore correct dietary intake and a balanced blood chemistry.

- Co-operation is vital, so undue pressure must be avoided.

- Weight gain alone is not necessarily a cure, and people with anorexia are often suspicious of doctors whom they see only being interested in them becoming fat.

- The goal is not to control the anorexic person, but relief of the suffering.

- Anorexia can be totally reversed, without lasting effects, but the person must want to be cured; and this means putting on weight without becoming 'fat'.

- Treatment started within one year of the onset of anorexia has a far greater chance of quick recovery.

- Treatment may be:
  —personal counselling, concentrating on adolescent conflict, interpersonal problems, and personal experiences of stress and failure
  —behaviour modification
  —trance therapy and hypnotherapy
  —group therapy
  —family counselling
  —cognitive therapy.

- Self-help groups, such as Anorexic Aid, offer help in much the same way as Alcoholics Anonymous.

- Education is essential, to learn about weight regulation and the effects of starvation on the body, where all the bodily systems are affected.

- Because of the physical effects of the illnesses, it is important that any treatment plan for a person with anorexia nervosa or bulimia nervosa includes nutritional management and nutritional counselling to begin to rebuild physical health and establish healthy eating practices.

DEALING WITH EATING DISORDERS

1. Establish effective communication.
2. Don't insist on increased intake of food.
3. Encourage outside help.
4. Don't pressure for weight gain.
5. Encourage self-action and responsibility.
6. Parents (or other relatives) may need counselling themselves, so that if they are putting their child under pressure to succeed they can be helped to remove that pressure.
7. Parents may need encouraging to work towards independence of their child.

PINPOINTING THE EARLY WARNING SIGNS

Here are some general warning signs to look for if you think someone has an eating disorder.

- Noticeable weight loss or weight gain, or extreme thinness or obesity.

- Finding excuses to skip meals.

- Unusual, ritualistic eating behaviour.

- Over-sensitivity to criticism.

- Tendency towards perfection.

- Unusual concern over changes in routine; not flexible or adaptable.

- Withdrawal from friends and activities.

- An unusual commitment or involvement in an activity (such as music or dance) to the exclusion of other activities.

- Conversation largely about food and weight.

- Intolerance of others.

- Unusual concern about school performance; grades are never good enough.

- Controlled communication; usually very proper, polite.

- May appear tense or too animated.

- Very controlled behaviour.

- Able to hide feelings.

- Low self-esteem (this may not be obvious at first).

- Preoccupation with food, weight (counting calories, excessive dieting).

- Claims of 'feeling fat' when weight is normal or low.

- Guilt and shame about eating.

- Frequent weighing.

- Evidence of binge-eating.

- Hoarding of food.

- Use of laxatives, diuretics, purgatives, emetics, excessive and punishing exercise.

- Secretive vomiting; leaving for the bathroom immediately after a meal.

- Moodiness, irritability and depression.

BEING CONCERNED ABOUT SOMEONE'S EATING DIFFICULTIES

Advice to relatives or other people concerned about another's eating disorders.

1. Be patient – eating disorders can be long-term problems even if the person is in therapy. Encourage the anorexic or bulimic to seek professional help.

2. If the person's eating habits are truly endangering his/her life, be insistent that professional help is sought.

3. Seek outside help for yourself. Find a support group, a counsellor, or other professional who has experience in helping families and friends cope with an eating disorder.

4. When discussing the problem with a person you suspect has an eating disorder (especially if it is for the first time), the reaction is often one of denial or perhaps even hostility.

5. Don't lay blame. This only reinforces the person's feelings of failure.

6. Try to ensure that you don't allow the person's problems to interfere with your normal functioning.

7. Let the person know that he/she is important to the family but not more so than any other family member.

8. Don't dwell on food-related discussions.

9. Encourage the person to get involved with non-food related activities.

10. Avoid commenting on the person's weight or appearance – your comments may not be taken in proper context.

11. The person with an eating disorder must feel that he/she has control over his/her daily routine. This can be very frustrating for those around the individual, but the situation often only becomes worse when it is perceived that someone else is trying to take that control away.

12. Be aware that low self-esteem is often a problem for those with eating disorders.

13. Learn everything you can about eating disorders. The more you know, the more you can understand.

SPECIFIC SIGNS OF ANOREXIA NERVOSA	SPECIFIC SIGNS OF BULIMIA NERVOSA
Significant weight loss in the absense of related illness.	Evidence of binge-eating.
Significant reduction in eating, coupled with a denial of hunger.	People report large amounts of food missing.
Dieting when not 'overweight'.	Frequent weight fluctuations.
Signs of starvation – thinning of hair; hair loss; apperance of fine raised, white hair on the body.	Evidence of purging (vomiting, laxative/diuretic abuse, emetics, frequent fasting).
Bloated feeling.	
Yellowish appearance of the palms or soles of feet.	Excessive exercise.
Dry, pasty skin. Amenorrhea.	Swelling of parotid glands under the jaw (caused by frequent vomiting).
Preference for foods of a certain texture or colour, compulsively arranging food, unusual mixtures of food.	

Fig. 4. The tell-tale signs of anorexia and bulimia.

CASE STUDIES

Samantha fights her anorexia

Samantha says, 'I started with a diet, but almost died. At 16, I weighed 110 pounds (7½ stone), but then a boy told me I wasn't asked to a school dance because I was fat. He was teasing, but I took it seriously. I started counting calories. First, I skipped lunch. When it came to summer and wearing a bikini I cut out breakfast. I obsessively weighed my food and calculated the calories I had consumed.

'By summer, my daily intake had plummeted to some 300 calories a day, and I now weighed 93 pounds (6½ stone). My knees, elbows and fingers often swelled uncomfortably; my finger-nails broke easily and my hair had split ends. When my friends and parents commented on my emaciated frame, I pointed to the 'ripples of fat' on my legs and stomach.

'I flatly refused to see a doctor until I fainted getting on the bus for school. In the fall, I cut my forehead; my parents took me to the casualty department. The doctor was appalled by my emaciation; he said I was suffering from anorexia nervosa and immediately admitted me to the hospital. I don't know how my family coped with it all. I think I screwed them all up with anxiety, in fact, the anxiety was worse for them than for me, for by that time I had gone past caring. I really couldn't believe there was anything wrong with me. I would have died if my parents hadn't cared, really cared. I'm not over it yet, and maybe never will be. A bit like an alcoholic, I suppose. But I'm fighting it.'

Barbara is a recovering bulimic

Barbara says, 'I'm 22 years old. I've had bulimia since I was 15, and I'm still dealing with it. I've cut out the laxatives, the amphetamines and the diuretics and I'm learning more about the field of eating disorders so that one day I can be proud to say that I am a "former" bulimic. I think it's important to realise the varying facets of bulimia.

'For those people who think that the binge-purge cycle merely means consuming all the food in the fridge at one sitting and then throwing it up – you're wrong. For me, binging entails very minute, picky behaviour. I allow myself an absurd number of "things" to eat on a given day; usually the number is less than 5. If I go over that number, I feel like I've totally crumbled and I have no self-control whatsoever. If I maintain the number or go below it, I am pleased with my determination and my ability to "maintain control". This idea of allowing myself a finite number of options for my daily diet is part of my bulimic behaviour.

'I never eat foods with high fat content, and subsequently I know I'm depriving myself of necessary protein and minerals that my body needs. In terms of purging, I exercise religiously, train on the college triathlon team. Here at university I maintain an outward image of having a "healthy lifestyle", being "competent" and "independent", when in reality, I'm starving myself and exercising on an empty stomach most of the time. Sometimes, if I know that I want to look "thin" on a given day, I will starve myself three or four days straight, eating very minimally, mostly liquids and vegetables with a high water content, and put up with the cold, blue fingertips, the dizziness, the lightheadedness, all for the sake of maintaining my facade of control.'

SUMMARY

- Anorexia nervosa and bulimia nervosa have assumed increased importance in today's society. The anxiety they generate in sufferers themselves and in other people, their relatives and carers, is high.

- Treatment for eating disorders can be given on an outpatient basis, but more serious cases need to be treated in hospital. Between five and twenty per cent of people die. About half recover; and about one quarter show improvement.

- People rarely die from bulimia, unless the purging leads to irreversible imbalance of the blood chemistry. The course is usually a waxing and waning one, with long periods of remission. The goal in both treatments is not control of the patient, but relief of suffering.

- The person suffering from anorexia needs as much understanding and psychological help as anyone suffering from one of the other anxiety states, for the overriding emotion is fear. But it is a fear which pushes the person further and further toward self-destruction.

- People with eating disorders are often overcome with guilt, so other people blaming them or telling them to pull themselves together only increases the guilt. Relatives are often stricken with guilt about eating disorders, and they need psychological support as much for themselves as for the person with the eating disorder.

8

Understanding the Anxiety of Sexual Difficulties

One of the most potent sources of anxiety is that surrounding sexuality and sexual difficulties. A satisfactory sex life increases energy and creates a sense of well-being. What produces anxiety is internal conflict and a sense of frustration.

Certain sexual dysfunctions will not be discussed here, because they fall outside the range of what could be considered normal dysfunctions. Neither will homosexuality be discussed. In 1973, following vigorous lobbying by gay activists, the American Psychiatric Association removed homosexuality as a diagnosis of mental illness from its *Diagnostic and Statistical Manual of Mental Disorders (DSM)*, as has the World Health Organisation's *International Classification of Mental and Behavioural Disorders* (1992). Homosexual people may experience any of the sexual difficulties experienced by heterosexual couples, and the anxiety they experience may be just as crippling.

Sexual problems may be classified as physiological, psychological and social in origin. Any given problem may involve all three categories; a physiological problem, for example, will produce psychological effects and these may result in some social maladjustment.

UNDERSTANDING HUMAN SEXUALITY

Human sexuality is concerned with the organs of sex and their functions; the sex impulses, instincts and drives; the thoughts, feelings and behaviours associated with sexual gratification, the attraction of one person to another, and the possibility of reproduction.

Sexuality is an essential part of one's personality, and cannot be separated from it. It is part of one's biological makeup, and includes one's perception of being male or female. Abnormal sexual behaviour is that which is destructive and harmful to one's self or others.

Identifying the characteristics of normal sexual response

Desire
Sexual fantasies and the urge to engage in sexual activity.

Excitement
Physiological stimulation through kissing and touch; a felt sense of pleasure; erection or vaginal lubrication; nipples of both sexes become erect, though this is more common in women; firming up of the clitoris, with venous engorgement of the lips of the vulva; rate of heartbeat and respiration increase and blood pressure rises.

Orgasm
Peaking of sexual pleasure, with release of sexual tension. Ejaculation occurs in the man, with emission of semen. The female experiences orgasm by strong sustained contractions of the uterus. Both men and women experience rise in blood pressure, and the heart rate increases, maybe up to 160 beats a minute. Orgasm lasts from three to twenty-five seconds and is associated with a slight clouding of consciousness.

Resolution (detumescence)
The blood leaves the sexual organs, bringing the body back to its resting state. Orgasm is followed by a sense of well-being, general and muscular relaxation. It may take a man several hours (a refractory period) before he can be sexually aroused to orgasm again. This does not always apply to women.

Understanding the male sexual function
- Concern (often amounting to severe anxiety) over the size of the penis is practically universal among men, but size has nothing to do with function.

- Ejaculation is the forceful propulsion of semen and seminal fluid into the urethra (the tube through which urine is voided from the bladder).

- The passing of seminal fluid as it passes through the prostate provides the man with a sensation of impending climax.

- The ejaculation is aided by the action of muscles of the pelvis and at the root of the penis.

- Erection depends on a complex interaction of the autonomic nervous system. Blood flows into the spongy tissues on the underside of the penis. Muscles at the base of the penis contract, so preventing the blood flowing back until ejaculation takes place.

- Impotence, or failure of the man to get or maintain an erection, can thus result from a number of causes, which may be psychological or physiological. If not enough hormones are pumped into the body, or if there is muscle weakness, or if there are problems with the blood supply, impotence may result.

Understanding the female sexual function

- The sexual organs of the female consist of the external sexual organs and the internal organs of reproduction.

- To accommodate the erect penis, the vaginal canal expands both in length and width.

- After the menopause the vagina loses much of its elasticity.

- The clitoris is the primary sexual organ, because orgasm depends on adequate clitoral stimulation.

- The clitoris has a nerve net that is proportionally three times as large as that of the penis.

- Many women describe the so-called 'G' spot, an area near the urethra, as giving great pleasure, enough to induce orgasm.

EXPLORING PHYSIOLOGICAL PROBLEMS OF SEXUAL FUNCTION

Physiological problems of a specifically sexual nature are rather few. Only a small minority of people suffer from diseases of or deficient development of the genitalia. Many people, however, at some time experience sexual problems that are by-products of other pathologies or injuries.

Anything that seriously interferes with normal bodily functioning generally causes some degree of sexual trouble. Fortunately, the great majority of physiological sexual problems are solved through medication or surgery. Generally, only those problems involving damage to the nervous system defy therapy.

EXPLORING PSYCHOLOGICAL PROBLEMS OF SEXUAL FUNCTION

Psychological problems constitute by far the largest category of sexual difficulties. They may be the product of socially induced inhibitions, faulty attitudes and ignorance, but sexual myths held by society are powerful influences. An example of the latter is the idea that good, mature sex must involve rapid erection, protracted coitus and simultaneous orgasm. Magazines, novels and sexual folklore reinforce these demanding ideals, which cannot always be met and hence give rise to anxiety, guilt and feelings of inadequacy.

A sexual dysfunction is a disturbance of the sexual response cycle – desire, excitement, orgasm and resolution – or caused by pain associated with sexual intercourse.

LOOKING AT PARTICULAR DISORDERS

Understanding disorders of sexual desire

The need for sexual contact and satisfaction varies greatly from person to person. Lack of desire may be an unconscious defence against fear of sex. Lack of desire can also be related to periods of stress or depression. Lack of sexual activity for a prolonged period can lead to suppression of sexual desire.

Sexual desire is a complex mix of biological drive, adequate self-esteem, previous experiences of good and bad sex, and the availability of a suitable partner.

Some people are brought up to believe that sex is all right for men, but for women it is disgusting and degrading, and only for the purpose of producing children. It might be thought that this is an attitude of an older generation and would not apply to the liberated young people of the last years of this century, but attitudes like that have a pernicious habit of hanging on from generation to generation.

Sexual aversion
When the prospect of sexual interaction with a sexual partner is associated with strong negative feelings and produces sufficient fear or anxiety that sexual activity is avoided. The dysfunction, when persistent, usually causes difficulties within the person and between couples. The aversion may be to a specific part of sex; genital contact (secretions, smell) may arouse feelings of disgust; kissing and touching on certain parts of the body may generate enough negative feelings to stop the process. The dividing line between a lack or loss of desire and aversion to sex is finely drawn, but sexual aversion has certain elements of phobia in it.

Freud postulated that sexual aversion was unresolved oedipal conflict, and fixation at the phallic stage. According to Freudian theory, some men who are fixated at the phallic stage believe that the vagina is something to be feared; that they will be castrated; that the vagina has teeth. Hence they avoid all contact with the female genitalia. Aversion may be attributed to traumatic sexual experiences when young, that have left the person carrying a load of guilt and shame.

Understanding disorders of sexual arousal
Male erectile disorder or dysfunction, also called **impotence** is divided into:

- Lifelong: never having had an erection that has culminated in vaginal penetration.

- Acquired: has successfully achieved vaginal penetration at some stage, but is later unable to do so.

- Situational: able to achieve penetration in one situation but not in another; for example, with a prostitute or with another man, but be impotent with his female sexual partner.

- Many men fear impotency, particularly as they reach middle-age.

- Many medical conditions produce physiological impotence, but these do not account for all cases of men for whom impotence is the dysfunction for which they seek help.

Impotence can be caused by a combination of factors, partly physical, partly psychological. Usually the physical problem will start first and gradually worsen. Secondary psychological fears and anxieties then begin to set in and sex becomes a very anxiety-provoking experience, sometimes coupled with depression.

Understanding disorders of orgasm

In males, orgasmic disorders or **retarded ejaculation** means that the man only achieves climax with great difficulty. Some practitioners make a distinction between orgasm and ejaculation, though the two are so bound together that it is difficult to make a clear distinction. Although not strictly an orgasmic disorder, **premature ejaculation** is closely connected in that both conditions are to do with climax. Retarded ejaculation may be due to the effects of drugs – certain anti-hypertensive drugs and tran-quillisers, for example. Recent excessive alcohol intake may also influence retarded orgasm.

Potential causes
For the man who has never been able to achieve orgasm (primary inhibited male orgasm) there may be a history of coming from a puritanical and rigid background, where sex equates with sin, where genitals are dirty and the whole process is laden with guilt. The same person may experience difficulty with intimacy in any shape or form.

Secondary ejaculatory inhibition may be a reflection of inter-personal difficulties, the sexual difficulty being the man's (unconscious) way of coping. For example, the female partner wishes to become pregnant, the man is ambivalent, so (again unconsciously) he becomes disabled and cannot achieve orgasm, although he may be perfectly able to do so through masturbation. At a deeper and more dynamic level, not achieving orgasm may be veiled hostility towards the woman, or towards all women.

Premature ejaculation is a common problem, especially for young males. Sometimes this is not the consequence of any psychological problem but the natural result of excessive tension in a male who has been sexually deprived. In such cases, more frequent intercourse (or masturbation) solves the problem. Premature ejaculation is difficult to define. Masters and Johnston say that a male suffers from premature ejaculation if he cannot delay ejaculation long enough to induce orgasm in a sexually normal female at least half the time.

Important points

It is more common than most people believe.
The cause is often something physical. It should not be dismissed as 'all in the mind'.
Almost every single case can be treated medically, reliably and inexpensively.

Physical factors

Hormone deficiency
A deficiency of testosterone and other hormones occurs in a small percentage of men with impotence.

Diabetes
Between 30% and 50% of diabetic men suffer from impotence. Among the effects of diabetes are high blood sugar levels, poor circulation, damaged nerve endings, narrowed arteries and high blood pressure.

Blocked arteries
The extra blood need for an erection may not be reaching the penis.

Leaking veins
To achieve and maintain an erection, veins must trap blood in the penis. Venous leaks are found to be the cause for a small number of men with impotence.

Psychological factors

Stress/anxiety
A man may experience normal erections in the early mornings but fail during sex with a partner.

'Male menopause'
The female menopause is well known. But some doctors say that a man can also suffer from a mid-life crisis, causing depression, hot flushes, lack of energy and low sex drive, night sweats and ciruculatory problems, leading to impotence.

False expectations
Expectations about performance found in the media – magazines, newspapers and television – lead to disappointment and despair if the reality seems quite different to the stereotypical image.

Fig. 5.   Summary of impotence.

Physical factors

Damaged nerves
Damage caused by spinal cord injuries, multiple sclerosis, and alcoholism, bladder and bowel surgery can also affect the nervous system.

Drugs
Impotence may be a side-effect of anti-depressants and anti-ulcer drugs. Drugs for the treatment of high blood pressure and even simple over-the-counter decongestant cold remedies have also been found to lead to impotence.

Alcohol
Small quantities often enhance a man's sexual response, but heavy or prolonged drinking can cause impotence.

Fig. 5.   (Continued).

Understanding sexual disorders which involve pain

Dyspareunia

This is persistent pain during intercourse. In women it is often associated with vaginismus (see below); the one may lead to the other. It is often found to be linked to pelvic disease, and is a common complaint in women who have been raped or sexually abused.

Pain after intercourse is thought to be due to violent uterine contractions during orgasm, in women who suffer from endometriosis. Post-menopausal women may experience pain through the thinning of the lining of the vagina and lack of lubrication. Some inexperienced females fear they cannot accommodate a penis without being painfully stretched. This is a needless fear since the vagina is not only highly elastic but enlarges with sexual arousal, so that even a small female can, if aroused, easily receive an exceptionally large penis. If the man proceeds with intercourse, irrespective of his partner's vaginal readiness, then pain is almost inevitable.

Dyspareunia can also occur in men, but is uncommon and usually associated with some medical condition, such as inflammation of the prostate. Persistent erection without ejaculation may also produce pain. Pain may sometimes be experienced at the moment of ejaculation.

Vaginismus

This is a recurrent or persistent, powerful and involuntary spasm of the pelvic muscles constricting the vagina so that penetration is painful or impossible. It may be due to anti-sexual conditioning or psychological trauma and serves as an unconscious defence against intercourse. While the woman may consciously wish to have intercourse, unconsciously there may be something preventing penile penetration. Rape or previous experiences of sexual abuse may set the scene for vaginismus. Painful physical examinations in the past can act in the same way. A final point is that where women feel unappreciated, and where sex is merely an act and not the sharing of love, then resentment may find an expression in vaginismus.

UNDERSTANDING TREATMENT FOR SEXUAL DYSFUNCTION

Treating men

Because there are a number of factors involved, the combination of treatments is varied for each man, but usually includes counselling. Where a physical cause is detected, explanation helps the man realise that the physical problem which caused the difficulty in the first place can be treated.

It is important not to presume that all cases have a common cause. For this reason it is best to view impotence as a medical problem. The doctor will treat this just like any other, and perform a full and proper diagnosis of the physical cause(s). Once this is done, treatment is usually very simple and offers a complete restoration of normal function.

Treating women

For females, sexual arousal dysfunction takes the form of persistent inability to attain or maintain adequate sexual excitement to completion. Women who experience difficulty in the excitement stage often experience problems with orgasm too. Less research has been done on sexual dysfunction in females than in males, though it has been suggested that women who experience sexual dysfunction are less aware of the physiological responses of their bodies during arousal.

Certain drugs – antihistamines for example – are known to lessen vaginal lubrication and interfere with arousal. An artificial lubricant is frequently useful for women who experience dryness.

Sex therapy, after the style of Masters and Johnson, deals with the couple; there is no credence given to the idea that only one of the couple is 'sick', needing to be 'cured'. The relationship is treated as a whole. The sexual dysfunction may be symptomatic of other relationship difficulties, and these may need to be brought into the open before the sexual difficulty can be resolved.

CASE STUDY

Gavin's impotence is a result of stress

'My name is Gavin. At the time I had difficulties with sex I was 28 years of age, an NCO stationed in Northern Ireland during the bloodiest time of the conflict. We had been married for six years, and had two children. Our sex life had been enjoyable, and both of us felt very fulfilled.

'The problem started when my erection went, soon after I entered Tracy. "It doesn't matter," said Tracy, meaning, "I'm not upset." But I didn't think of it like that. I took it that she was losing interest. I felt deflated and that my masculinity was on the line.

'The situation continued for about two months. Sometimes we managed to achieve intercourse, but often couldn't. I knew that any official 'reporting sick' would go on my records, so I approached a local doctor I was friendly with. "Stress," said the doctor with conviction. "Look at what you've been through these last nine months. All those deaths and bombings. Sex is often the first sign of the body giving you warning."'

'I felt a great weight roll off me. I talked it over with Tracy. She told me that she wasn't losing interest, but didn't want to put any pressure on me. We found pleasure through oral sex and masturbation. Soon afterward, the unit was returned to England, and my erection difficulties cleared up. Life again was great!'

SUMMARY

- This chapter has been a brief introduction to human sexuality, and how dysfunction can create anxiety. Related to this is how anxiety can create sexual difficulties. Sexual difficulties are often associated with high anxiety, for they strike at the very heart of femininity and masculinity.

- Sexuality deals with everything that relates to or is affected by sex, the biology and the psychology of sex, and all the thoughts, feelings, and behaviours connected with sexual gratification and reproduction, including the attraction of one person to another. Sexuality is an essential part of personality, and includes how we perceive ourselves as being masculine or feminine.

- Sexual problems may be classified as physiological, psychological and social in origin.

- Sexual dysfunction involves both people in the relationship, and therapy must consider both, within the total relationship.

- Sexual dysfunctions are not readily talked about, and because of this they are cloaked in secrecy and are often the butt of sick jokes, a fact that does not make their disclosure any easier. This lack of understanding is a powerful reason why many people do not seek professional help. Yet if the experts are to be believed, many people experience difficulty at some-time in their lives.

9

Coping with Illness and Trauma

In this chapter the following will be considered:

- pain

- depression

- death and bereavement

- major disasters

- suicide.

Physical and psychological disorders often result from the anxiety of not being able to cope with the emotional demands of daily living. One of the major causes of anxiety is the sudden onset of an illness or an accidental injury. As a consequence, the anxiety people experience may show itself in emotional or **psychosomatic** disorders. Psychosomatic refers to the constant and inseparable interaction of the **psyche** (mind) and the **soma** (body). The term is most commonly used to refer to illnesses in which the manifestations are primarily physical but with at least a partial emotional cause or reason.

Disease and injury are crises in the lives of many people. How they cope with the anxiety generated is crucial to their recovery, and recovery relies very much on the presence and attitude of significant others, particularly family members, a supportive environment and the attitude of others around. In Chapter 10 the issue of the anxiety of those who are engaged in long-term care will be discussed.

UNDERSTANDING THE LINK BETWEEN PAIN AND ANXIETY

Pain is frequently linked to anxiety. Sufferers from pain disorder, where nothing seems to relieve the pain, may experience acute anxiety or a state of panic. In an attack of pain the fight/flight reaction is triggered, producing feelings of anger, fear and anxiety. When pain becomes persistent and chronic, 'stress reaction' occurs, in which the delicate blood chemistry balance is disturbed, thereby increasing the anxiety.

Depression, insomnia and helplessness, in addition to anxiety, frequently accompany chronic pain. As a result of pain, some people become so withdrawn that they exclude others from their world.

The occurrence of disease and its associated pain is, to many, a black day on a calendar; a crossroads to which they have been pushed by some unseen force over which they had no control. And the painful road they now tread seems to lead on only to a bleak land of pain which threatens to engulf them in its blackness.

Learning to manage pain
Sometimes pain cannot be cured, but it can usually be managed and controlled. This section will not deal with painkillers, but with one technique which has proved to be successful. Pain interferes with rest and sleep, and lack of sleep is often a major contributor to suffering. Relaxation techniques, taught and practised when pain is absent, help to reduce physical and mental tension.

> **Sufferers who use imaging, combining it with deep relaxation, acquire a powerful double-edged strategy to control their pain.**

EXERCISE

Learning to manage your pain
For this exercise sit in a comfortable chair or lie on the bed. Imagine you have a migraine; it is agonising, you find it difficult to concentrate and you feel sick. Feel the symptoms.

1. Now focus your whole attention on one specific spot in your head. Feel the pulse beating in the spot. Let the beat become increasingly forceful. Let your whole head take on the beat.

2. Now gradually let the pressure ease. Breathe deeply. Let your

body start to relax, starting from the head. Let the feeling of peace fill your whole body.

3. When you have completed the exercise, rest for a while.

4. When you get up stretch, yawn and gently reorientate yourself to your surroundings.

5. You may substitute any part of the body for the migraine.

The next time you experience pain try this exercise and realise that you do have a method of managing pain.

UNDERSTANDING DEPRESSION WITH ANXIETY

Depression is one of the **mood** disorders. Mood is a predominant emotion that colours the person's entire well-being. The signs and symptoms are sustained over a period of time, during which they tend to recur in a periodic cycle; there is also a marked and definite change in the person's habitual functioning.

People with anxiety may suffer from a change in thinking and in bodily functions. The change in thinking includes worry, dread, reduced concentration, forgetfulness and irritability, with mood change, for example depression and insomnia with nightmares.

Enduring sleeplessness

For some people, sleeplessness is a cross upon which they feel crucified nightly. Many of us become anxious when just one night's sleep is disturbed, but for those for whom sleep is but a dream, life is dogged by what they cannot enjoy. Such people constantly live on the edge of acute anxiety.

Sleep is disturbed in both anxiety and depression. In anxiety the person has difficulty getting off to sleep; in depression the typical complaint is early morning waking with inability to get back to sleep, often accompanied by dark and foreboding thoughts.

A lady telephoned me recently asking to buy a replacement of one of my relaxation tapes, given to her by her daughter many years ago. 'I've played it every night since, and as I suffer from bad migraines and arthritis, I don't think I could have a good night's sleep without it.' The moral of this is, find what suits you and use it regularly.

Coping with depression

Depression, coupled with anxiety, drives the person as in the treadmill, yet at the same time throws him or her into limbo, that state of despair and isolation where the person feels cut off from anything that offers hope. (*Counselling in Rehabilitation*, Further Reading.) One of the most distressing anxieties to live with is the ever-present threats of suicide. Many people who suffer from depression get so pulled down by it that they see this as the only way out (see the section on suicide below).

Living with someone who suffers from anxiety is stressful; living with someone who suffers from depression is emotionally draining. Anxiety is infectious, in that other people start to feel wound up; depression is infectious, in that people start to respond to the depressed person's mood by becoming sad and low themselves. In both instances, anxiety is generated within, for example, relatives, as they begin to feel that their control is being sapped from them and their lives taken over.

EXERCISE

Learning to manage sleeplessness

1. If you are beset by fears, face them.

2. Get up, and write the fears down in a notebook. Setting them down in this way may be just enough to rob them of their power over you.

3. Answer the question, 'Why are my fears so terrible?'

4. Are you really as exhausted as your mind tells you?

5. Concentrate on being comfortable in bed, not on falling asleep.

6. Listen to some soothing music. Let the music speak to you by way of images.

7. Watch any thoughts that come, but remember, they are only thoughts and thoughts cannot kill you.

UNDERSTANDING THE ANXIETY OF DEATH AND BEREAVEMENT

There is no more potent a loss-source than death. There is trauma in death: the trauma of final separation. Loss is sometimes anticipated; very often it is totally unexpected. Grieving is the natural response to loss, and grief is the price we pay for loving. The absence of grief suggests abnormality, though we should be careful not to judge other people by the grief we feel.

There is more to bereavement than grieving for the actual physical loss of the person. When a loved one dies, a hole is left somewhere in the emotions. This hole, according to some accounts, is never filled. It is trite to say, 'Time heals'. Time does not heal. We just get used to living with a hole in the heart.

It would be understandable that death could be a major event in precipitating anxiety or depression, but the feelings of loss may not always be within the conscious memory of the person who still carries the loss around (see Case Studies).

UNDERSTANDING THE ANXIETY OF MAJOR DISASTERS

One of the anxiety disorders is post-traumatic stress disorder (PTSD). This is brought about by exposure to an exceptional mentally or physically distressing event which generates feelings of intense terror, fear or helplessness. Such events are generally outside the range of normal human experience and would be distressing to almost anyone. After World War II, the condition became known as 'concentration-camp syndrome'. Three such catastrophic events are the Lockerbie plane crash, the Hillsborough football disaster and the Clapham train disaster.

The person experiences frequent flashbacks and may exhibit increased irritability, have exaggerated startled reactions and have sleeping difficulties including nightmares.

People who feel they are unable to regain control of their lives, or who experience the symptoms set out in Figure 6 *for more than a month*, should consider seeking help from a mental health professional.

Probable indicators of PTSD
1. Anxiety and fear, especially when exposed to events or situations reminiscent of the trauma.

EXAMPLES OF STRESSFUL EVENTS	EXAMPLES OF STRESSORS
Serious threat to life or physical integrity.	Rape or assault.
Serious threat or harm to one's children, spouse, or other close relatives and friends.	Military combat.
Sudden destruction of home or community.	Natural manufactured catastrophes.
Seeing another person who has recently been, or is being, seriously injured or killed as the result of accident or violence.	Physical or sexual abuse.

Fig. 6.   Identifying examples of major traumatic events.

2. Appetite changes.

3. Avoiding activities, places or people that remind the person of the event.

4. Crying spontaneously.

5. Decisions are difficult to make.

6. Depression, sadness, with low energy.

7. Despair and hopelessness.

8. Edgy, being easily startled or becoming overly alert.

9. Feeling 'scattered' and unable to focus on work or daily activities.

10. Irritability, easily agitated, or angry and resentful.

11. Memory problems including difficulty in remembering aspects of the trauma.

12. Numb, withdrawn, disconnected or feeling different from others.

13. Protective of, or fearful for, the safety of loved ones.

14. Recurring thoughts or nightmares about the event.

15. Sleep disturbed, can't get to sleep, nightmares, waking early.

HELPING PEOPLE COPE WITH DISASTERS

The following points can help alleviate suffering:

- Planning for crises can reduce anxiety when they do occur.

- Dealing with a crisis demands fast decision-making and action, clear lines of communication and easy access to all available information.

- People who are in the front line of coping with the crisis need support and personal supervision during, and ideally on, day 2, 3 or 4 following the incident.

- Bereaved relatives who have an opportunity to see the dead body usually grieve more constructively.

- Acute PTSD requires immediate action; allowing the person to ventilate feelings is vital, but as so often is the case, it may be many weeks before the person starts to feel the impact of the trauma.

- Group counselling is recommended by some authorities. The comradeship within the group creates a feeling of safety.

COPING WITH THE TRAUMA OF SUICIDE

Why do people kill themselves?

The common link between people who kill themselves is the belief that suicide is the only solution to a set of overwhelming feelings. The attraction of suicide is that it will finally end these unbearable feelings. The tragedy of suicide is that intense emotional distress often blinds people to alternative solutions, yet other solutions are almost always available.

Many people experience feelings of loneliness, depression, helplessness and hopelessness from time to time. The death of a family member, the break-up of a relationship, blows to our self-esteem, feelings of worthlessness, and/or major financial setbacks are serious events which all of us may have to face at some point in our lives. Because each person's emotional makeup is unique, each of us responds to situations differently.

In considering whether a person may be suicidal, it is imperative that the crisis be evaluated from that person's perspective. What may seem of minor importance to one person can be extremely distressful to another. Regardless of the nature of the crisis, if a person feels overwhelmed there is the danger that suicide may seem an attractive solution.

Depression and suicide

Depression is the chief cause of suicide. People who are suffering from situational depression (sometimes called 'reactive') very often respond positively to counselling. Clinical (also called 'endogenous') depression is difficult to handle with counselling but usually responds to medical intervention. Loneliness often leads to situational depression. Relationship difficulties may also lead to depression and are a common cause of suicide and para-suicide (suicide attempts). Chad Varah, of the Samaritans, says that befriending often swings the ambivalent person in favour of living and towards finding an alternative to death.

COUNTERING MYTHS ABOUT SUICIDE

Myth 1: 'You have to be crazy even to think about suicide'

Many people have thought of suicide from time to time. Most suicides and suicide attempts are made by intelligent, temporarily confused individuals who are expecting too much of themselves, especially in the midst of a crisis.

Myth 2: 'Once a person has made a serious suicide attempt, that person is unlikely to make another'

Persons who have made prior suicide attempts may be at greater risk of actually committing suicide; for some, suicide attempts may seem easier a second or third time.

Myth 3: 'If a person is seriously considering suicide, there is nothing you can do'

Most suicide crises are time-limited and based on unclear thinking. Persons attempting suicide want to escape from their problems. Instead, they need to confront their problems directly in order to find other solutions – solutions which can be found with the help of concerned individuals who support them through the crisis period, until they are able to think more clearly.

Myth 4: 'Talking about suicide may give a person the idea'

The crisis and resulting emotional distress will already have triggered the thought in a vulnerable person. Your openness and concern in asking about suicide will allow the person experiencing pain to talk about the problem, which may help reduce his or her anxiety. This may also allow the person with suicidal thoughts to feel less lonely or isolated, and perhaps a bit relieved.

Myth 5: 'People who commit suicide are people who were unwilling to seek help'

Studies of suicide victims have shown that more than half had sought medical help in the six months before their deaths.

CASE STUDIES

June and Ian experience symbolic loss

The two extracts from case notes of June and Ian show how feelings of loss transcend memory.

June

When June's sister-in-law of whom she was very fond and felt like a sister, dies, the grief she feels seems exaggerated and prolonged. Gradually it emerges that the recent grief has reawakened the sense of loss she felt about her mother's death, when June was aged 2. Now aged 50, she has no conscious recollection of her mother.

Ian

Ian is in his mid-50s when his father dies. His mother had died four years previously. Half seriously he says to his counsellor, 'I'm now an orphan.' As the truth of these words sinks in, he begins to weep. 'It's the first time in my life I've ever been depressed. I feel as if I'm in a hole in the ground and I'm covered over with a grey blanket. It's very dark and cold.'

One of the curious things about sadness is that, as a piece of string dipped into wax will gradually collect more and more wax, one sadness attracts others to it. In Ian's case, the loss of his father attracts some hitherto unexpressed sadness about the loss of his mother. But that is not all.

Over a number of counselling sessions it becomes clear that there are other losses that are not so obvious as the sadness over his parents. A brother had died before Ian was born. Ian had always felt deprived of his brother's love. He had never felt much love for his only other brother, several years older than himself.

Another factor is that the death of his parents, and particularly his father's death, has come at a time when he is having to make some personal adjustments to his own 'middle age'. Ian is carrying the accumulated weight of actual and symbolic loss. His depression – which does not require medication – begin to lift after a few weeks, though he does find that being brought into contact with the sadness of others reawakens his own for many months afterwards.

Susan experiences flashbacks of her rape

Susan says, 'I was raped when I was 25 years old. For a long time I spoke about the rape in a detached way, as though it was some-thing that happened to someone else. It was all up in my head. I was very aware that it had happened to me, but there just was no feeling.

'I sort of coasted along for a while. Then I started having flashbacks. They came over me like a huge wave of the sea. I was terrified. Suddenly I was reliving the rape. Every moment was startling. I felt like my entire head was moving, shaking, but that wasn't so at all. I would get very flushed, or have a very dry mouth and my breathing changed.

'I was held in suspension. I wasn't aware of the cushion on the chair that I was sitting in or that my arm was touching a piece of furniture. I was in a bubble, just kind of floating. It was scary. Having a flashback can wring you out. You're really shaken. The rape happened the week before Christmas and I feel like some monster around the anniversary date.'

Trevor experiences a build-up of stress

Trevor says, 'I'm a traffic policeman, and by the nature of the job I'm often the first person on the scene of a traffic accident. In a space of just over one week I was involved in six such accidents. What caused me the greatest stress was having to tell the relatives of the dead person.

'Two weeks after the last incident I asked for help. My sleep was disturbed by dreams, and flashbacks happened during the day. I'm normally a calm sort of chap, but now I was irritable with the wife and children. I had no appetite. Two sessions of counselling helped me to regain control. All the counsellor did was allowed me to talk and express the horror. I was also taught how to relax.'

SUMMARY

- Illness or accidental injury are events which frequently create acute anxiety, for they throw us into unfamiliar surroundings, and generate feelings of helplessness and dependency. To someone who is normally fit and well, the anxiety of being ill can be overwhelming and difficult to contain. For some people the fact that they are ill generates fear of not being perfect and in control of their own lives.

- The major difference between emotional and physical illnesses which involves the person becoming a patient is that they cannot be seen. Anxiety, depression and PTSD are invisible illnesses, which often means that they are labelled as 'all in the mind', or imaginary. This places sufferers in a double-bind. If they speak out they are often not believed; if they don't they cannot get relief. Not seeing something does not mean that it does not exist. We cannot see electricity, but we can judge its effects. In the same way we can judge the effects of crippling conditions such as PTSD.

- Suicide is possibly the ultimate trauma against one's self. The possibility of suicide threatens to destabilise even the most stable of families. The trauma of the death leaves a permanent scar in the memory of the family. An understanding of what suicide means will help to dispel myths about this trauma.

10

Coping with the Anxiety of Long-Term Caring

Illness is a stressor which affects the whole family. However mature and together a family is, when one of the family becomes ill everybody else is likely to be caught up in a web of anxiety. The unknown is frightening, and even a minor illness can create anxiety of mammoth proportions. Serious illness, accident or trauma can affect everybody with crippling anxiety.

There is another face to this, however. Not all family members are sympathetic or understand what is happening. Lack of understanding can cause them to make light of whatever it is the person is complaining of. Such comments as, 'It's all in mind', 'Pull yourself together', 'There are many worse off than you', do not help. In fact, they increase the anxiety felt by the person with the illness. Making light of something may be one way of coping, but it does little for the person concerned.

UNDERSTANDING THE EFFECTS OF LONG-TERM CARING

All the topics discussed in Chapter 9 have implications for relatives or other carers. Coping with a loved one who is in constant pain is likely to reinforce the relatives' helplessness, for there is a natural tendency to want to do something to alleviate the suffering.

Living with someone whose moods are mercurial and unpredictable is unnerving. Being involved with someone who has been raped, and continues to suffer nightmares, who cannot leave the house unless unaccompanied, and whose life has been turned upside down, is like sharing a living hell. Being the relative of someone who mutilates him or herself, or who repeatedly threatens suicide, means that everybody's fight/flight response is constantly on red alert.

What of the anxiety of relatives who can only sit on the side lines and watch as their beloved daughter slowly starves herself so that she becomes nothing more than skin and bone?

Looking at particular difficulties

These and many more examples illustrate the hidden mountain of anxiety of relatives, but there is an equally large group of people, long-term carers, many of whom struggle on from year to year without respite, or only minimal relief. This chapter will explore some situations of long-term carers and the burden of unremitting anxiety they carry. Long-term caring for someone presents particular difficulties, mainly because the carer can see no way out, no end to the long road that lies ahead.

CASE STUDY

Jim and Hazel live with multiple sclerosis

For the purpose of this chapter we will follow a couple called Jim and Hazel, aged 45. They had been married for twenty-five years, have three children and were looking forward to an easier life. They were expecting their first grandchild. Jim was making it up the career ladder as a foreman in a tool-making works. Hazel had started work as a receptionist in a doctor's surgery. For the first time in their married life they had started to put money away, and were able to enjoy holidays, usually travelling by car.

Jim visited his GP and said, 'I'm worried. I keep dropping things. About a month ago I stumbled and fell at work. My leg just gave way. Then I had pins and needles in the same leg. I was worried, I can tell you. And I get so tired. Hazel has to wake me up to go to bed. And my eyes feel funny; things don't look quite the same, sort of double.'

After tests and examinations, the specialist told Jim that he had multiple sclerosis (MS). Jim didn't know much about it, but Hazel knew a bit more, and the prospect looked bleak. While it is true that MS is a disease that incapacitates some people, and ties them to a wheelchair or confines them to bed, to be looked after either in hospital or by devoted relatives, others do not progress quite so dramatically down the path to chronic disability. Early disturbances are likely to involve sight, movement and sensation. Although in many cases these early symptoms disappear, in other instances there is steady deterioration. So it was with Jim.

Jim's story

'I had my good periods and bad, and the bad times gradually got longer and more frequent. I had always been a very independent and active man. I had completely modernised our house, and always repaired my car. Over the ten years from the time MS was diagnosed, I had to give up work and could no longer drive the car. This really got to me, for I had to rely on other people to take me around and I hated that.

'I swore I'd never be an invalid, and how I struggled, often ending up in tears of frustration. Gradually I lost all dignity, but as if that wasn't enough, the moods nearly drove Hazel mad. One day I'd be in deep depression and the next up in the clouds – euphoria, they call it. At other times I wouldn't know where I was, or who Hazel was. I love reading, but even that is difficult to concentrate on at times. My memory is shot to bits.

'Now I'm permanently in a wheelchair. I used to swim and play a lot of sports, and when I look at my legs and arms I could weep. Telling my story has taken a lot out of me, for my speech is not very clear now. I know I feel sorry for myself, but . . . !'

Hazel's story

'When the specialist said "MS", I felt faint and sick. I knew something about it because a girl-friend of mine had it and it went on for years. How would Jim cope with it; how would I? We both carried on working as long as we could. Jim gave up before me. I made all sorts of excuses to carry on, but the truth is I couldn't face being at home with him all day. But in the end I had to. Jim couldn't get up the stairs without help, and when he was up, he was stuck there. We tried joking about it: "Oh, the grand old Duke of York," we would sing, but after a time that wore thin.

'We moved a bed downstairs. Then there was his functions. He couldn't hold his urine, and that made him feel bad. That bit didn't worry me so much, but he felt it. I used to go to bed exhausted, but couldn't sleep. All I could see was years of this, him getting worse and me getting more depressed, for depressed I certainly was.

'Normally a quiet and considerate man, Jim gradually became demanding and aggressive, which always led to tears from him. I would like to say I kept sweet and kind, but I didn't. We often ended up shouting at each other, then I felt bad and had a good cry.

'If I'm honest, what really got to me was what happened to our love life. We had always enjoyed sex, and enjoyed giving each other pleasure. In fact, in the early days soon after the MS was diagnosed, we started having difficulty when Jim couldn't get an erection. He wouldn't talk about that, but it was devastating. To him it was the final insult to his manhood. I tried to satisfy him in other ways, but it was never the same. We stopped sleeping together after about three years. Now I'm his nurse, and there are no sexual feelings between us; just a peck on the cheek. I feel so sad.

'The children? I insisted that they went for counselling, for they were terrified that MS could be inherited. They were put right on that score. They've been wonderful, and as Jim has got worse they've really rallied round. One or other will take him out in the car, although recently he hasn't even wanted that.

'We've talked about death, and he knows that it could come any time. He told me to find another "real man". That's how it's been the last ten years. I wonder how much more I can take.'

COPING WITH CHILDREN WITH ILLNESS AND DISABILITY

In the above case study of Jim and Hazel, we saw that long-term caring for an adult presents difficulties and creates anxieties. Caring for a child who is seriously ill or disabled creates a different set of problems and anxieties.

CASE STUDY

In Chapter 6 we looked briefly at Betty, and Catherine, her daughter with Down's syndrome. Much has been done over recent years to 'normalise' people like Catherine, by bringing them out of institutions and into the community; this was not so forty years ago.

Betty's Down's syndrome daughter
'Nothing went wrong with the pregnancy, my third. Catherine arrived on time and David, my husband, was there. It was a home delivery, and all went well. From the start, Cathering was adored by David and the other two and like them she was a 'good' baby. I began to feel a bit anxious when Catherine's weight gain was so slow. But she seemed healthy, with lovely skin. Was there something wrong with my milk? The clinic thought not and reassured me that some babies are like that.

'Everything collapsed around us when I visited the clinic when Catherine was eight months old. The doctor wanted to come and talk with David and me about Catherine, as her development seemed a bit slow.

'The doctor was kindness itself, and he led us gently forward to his announcement that Catherine was a Down's baby.[1] The scene is etched on my memory as if with the strongest acid. The room started to spin and I was in danger of fainting, and would have, had I not sat down. "She might not live," said the doctor, as did the specialist from whom we asked a second opinion.

'They told us all they knew about Down's, and said we might like to think about putting Catherine into care. Yes, of course we thought about it, but dismissed it. She was already part of our family, and our faith was such that we believed there was a reason somewhere and that we would be given the strength to deal with whatever lay ahead. Apart from the second opinion, we accepted Catherine as she was, a delightful baby who smiled at everybody.

'All sorts of descriptive words come to my mind about how we felt, none could adequately convey our feelings. One of the over-whelming reactions was of utter isolation, knowing that we had a handicapped baby. What did we know about bringing up such a baby? All the information we found was a booklet which painted a gloomy picture of such children. The one bit of advice, if it was needed, was give the child plenty of love and she will reward you a thousand times over.

'I don't want to dwell on the heartache, nor dismiss it, neither do I want to trivialise what was a major event in our lives, but we picked ourselves up and got on with life, determined to be all that we could be to our three children. We wanted to move on, not to remain stuck in what we knew could not be changed.

'So how has it been over the years? Both David and I took things philosophically, but that didn't stop me from being anxious about how to handle Catherine; how to integrate her into the family; what effect it might have on the others having a handi-capped sister. What did the future hold for us? Would she be like the doctors said, not able to care for herself? Would she ever be able to do any of the ordinary things other children did and we

---

[1] John Langdon-Down 1828–1896, was a physician of renown who, in 1868 established a private home for mentally deficient children at Normansfield, Hampton Wick.

took for granted? My biggest worry was what people would think. I know that's silly, but that's me.

'When I fell pregnant with Sheila I was anxious a bit that she would be all right, but she was; as was Paul when he was born when Catherine was three. I'm glad I had the other two, for they helped to restore my sense of self-worth and they helped Catherine as they all grew up together.

'Catherine started going to a special school when she was 5, and it was then I really accepted that she was as she was. Looking back I think we all coped well and whatever the demands, the compensations were far more. I'm sure I've been over-protective, but that didn't stop me helping to make the decision that Catherine be taken into care when she was 16. She is still in care, and I still feel responsible for her and still feel guilty. I don't think that will ever change. Mothers are not suddenly endowed with superhuman or supernatural gifts merely because children are born to them. As a mother of a handicapped child I felt doubly vulnerable and doubtful of my ability to rear Catherine with sensitivity while still coping with my own feelings of shock and dismay.

'Now, I can look back with some degree of objectivity. I knew full well that if Catherine was to receive the care and stimulation she needed to grow and develop, some sacrifices would have to be made. I knew, or rather sensed, that having Catherine could lead to jealousy from David and the other children. The unconscious decision I made was that as far as possible, their needs would not be sacrificed. If anybody had to give up, it would be me.

'As far as possible I tried not to make Catherine my favourite, for I knew this could throw David and the others into an opposite camp and I wanted a united family, not a divided one. Perhaps more than all, I was determined not to isolate David. Our relationship has survived much, and we were united in our love and care for Catherine.

'Finally, one of the things we, David and I, worked hard at was not to make the other children feel either guilty or responsible for Catherine. They all have their thoughts and feelings about their sister, naturally, but as David and I are now getting older, we know that if Catherine survives us she will be well-provided for and the decision we made when she was 16 was the right one. At the time David and I were broken-hearted, and I was consumed with regret and reproached myself for making the decision. I cried for weeks.

'Catherine has brightened not only our lives but the lives of many other people; her unconditional love has kept us going during times of near despair. I can look back and feel that those early years, which stretched far beyond the normal, laid the foundation of her personality. So, in spite of the terrible guilt, I do console myself with having done the best I knew how.'

SUMMARY

- Illness and disability affect the whole family, even though the effects are not always obvious. Although most authorities agree that relatives, caught up in day-to-day caring, need a great deal of understanding support, that support is often not available, or relatives do not know where to get it.

- Stress and anxiety, coupled with the isolation which long-term caring inevitably brings, plus the lack of time and opportunity for relief-giving relaxation, lower the body's defences against disease, making carers more prone to illness. Anxiety and guilt are often present because of the conflict between the need (and the wish) to care, and the equally powerful wish and desire that the responsibility be removed. Removing a disabled person to hospital, or other establishment, does not remove the feelings of responsibility, nor does it remove all strain.

- Many long-term carers feel the anxiety of not having enough money to meet basic needs, and feel they belong to a disadvantaged group. Long-term caring must strike a balance between respecting the person being cared for, and the needs of the carer and others in the family.

11

Changing the Way You Think to Combat Anxiety

Many of us get caught up in negative thinking, but manage to function reasonably well. When we are engulfed in anxiety it seems almost impossible to reverse the process and think positively. But thought-reversal is only part of the story. Changing faulty thinking patterns must go hand-in-hand with changing behaviour.

> **Positive thinking is believing in yourself, and having faith in your abilities.**

It is having confidence in yourself without being arrogant and self-opinionated.

UNDERSTANDING THE POWER OF THOUGHT

In a way, thinking can be regarded as behaviour; it is something we do, and it influences how we feel and behave. At the same time, due note must be taken of feelings. They cannot be ignored. If we do, then we could become like Mr Spock of *Star Trek* fame. On the other hand a person who is all heart, who prefers feeling to thinking, is only living on half his or her potential.

Such was Betty, the lady in Chapter 10. Betty was ruled by her heart and felt things very keenly, too much so. She took to heart what people said and felt slights very deeply. She tended to blame herself for everything that went wrong. In fact, everything was filtered through feelings. It was almost impossible for her husband or children to have a debate with her, for whenever a contrary point of view was expressed, she took it as a personal slight. Her thinking function was undeveloped, and this proved quite a handicap. Yet people loved her because she was so warm and caring.

Using the power of thought

In her counselling she was encouraged to look at her thinking processes; in counselling it would be called 'cognitive therapy'. This type of therapy was developed by Aaron Beck, who puts forward the view that behaviour is primarily determined by what that person thinks. Cognitive therapy works on the premise that thoughts of low self-worth are incorrect and are due to faulty learning. What Betty came to realise was that she heavily engaged in negative thinking. She almost wallowed in dwelling on what had gone wrong, and what could go wrong. As a consequence, her fight/flight response was often on red alert. Yet Betty found it nigh impossible to change her thinking pattern; it seemed easier (her words) to stick to the old ways than to grow new ones.

CASE STUDY

Andrew Fisher thinks he's going to die

'I had been treated by my family doctor for about two weeks, for palpitations and I was worried that I might be heading for a coronary. The doctor prescribed suitable medication but the symptoms persisted. An electrocardiogram (ECG) revealed nothing abnormal.

'My wife called the family doctor in the middle of the night because I had a panic attack in bed, with racing pulse and palpitations. I was admitted as an emergency, but nothing physically wrong was found.

'One of my neighbours died of a coronary about two months previously. He had complained of chest pains before going to bed. His wife woke to find him dead. I was terrified that it might happen to me. Whenever I thought about it my heart started racing and I felt breathless.

'The doctor explained to me, quite simply, the fight/flight response. "The body produces adrenaline, so it's all tied up with that. Adrenaline prepares the body to fight or to run away. You know that when you are angry or afraid, your heart starts to beat faster, well that's what this is all about. The adrenaline is operating and if you do run away, or you stand and fight, the body uses up all the extra adrenaline and your heart rate returns to normal. If you don't do either of those, the adrenaline takes longer to be absorbed but you will experience the physical signs which people call palpitations."

'Quite frankly, I was sceptical, thinking the doctor was fobbing me off, so he loaned me a book on stress. Explaining the fight/ flight response was one of the major factors in helping me take control. I realised that I had been misinterpreting what was going on in my body, and that all this had been triggered by my thinking.

'I was taught a relaxation technique which I was encouraged to use frequently. My breathing was shallow and rapid, so they taught me to control that by regulated breathing and breathing from the abdomen, which helped a great deal.'

(Behaviour therapy combined with cognitive therapy is referred to as 'cognitive-behaviour therapy. The behavioural part aims to give clients control over what is happening, rather than feeling that they are out of control, by confronting the feared situation, person, or feeling.)

Andrew's marriage was difficult, so one of the challenges was for him to enter into marriage counselling and to work through some of the feelings involved there. Mrs Fisher was a carping, dominant woman who, herself, only agreed to enter counselling on account of previously undisclosed incestuous abuse by her father.

Another fear – not previously articulated – was that when his only son went to boarding school he (Andrew) would be forgotten. When David came home for the Christmas holidays, and was full of enthusiasm for the school, and he made it plain that Andrew still meant a lot to him, Andrew was reassured.

Discussing Andrew

Andrew was caught up in negative thinking. 'David won't want me any more.' 'I must have a bad heart.' 'Our marriage is falling apart and it's all my fault.' 'I can't do my job properly, so I'll get the sack.' Getting Andrew to change his thought pattern wasn't easy. The major, and the most urgent, was the panic about his heart. Explanation, medication, relaxation and talking about his fears, plus a great deal of support and helping him (and his wife and son) to understand the stressors that had led up to the first panic attack, were enough to reassure them all. His marriage, although certainly shaky, survived and David did well.

UNDERSTANDING THE THOUGHTS, FEELINGS AND BEHAVIOUR CYCLE

Thinking, feeling and behaving are three ways we make contact with the world. They are not discrete functions, held in watertight compartments; they are interlinked. When our prime focus is thinking, feeling and behaving are affected by what we think. When we are immersed in feelings, thinking and behaving are influenced.

Behaving is influenced by what we think and feel.

Seeing the negative cycle

Terry and Meg had an argument. 'How long have I been waiting for you to repair that work top? Six months! And what do you say? "I'll do it tomorrow." I'm fed up, right up to the teeth. You're hopeless.' Terry slammed out and walked off down the road. 'Hi, mate!' said an acquaintance, 'what's the matter? Got the world on your shoulders? You look like an old man.' Terry was walking with his head down and his shoulders hunched.

The cycle was something like this.

Angry feelings → *thoughts*: I'm useless. A rotten husband → weighed down, carrying a burden.

How could Terry reverse the process? By restructuring his thinking along the lines of:

Feelings: I am angry → *thoughts*: I did promise, and I haven't kept to it – *behaviour*: I'll go back and we'll agree a date → *restructured thoughts*: now, then, Terry, my boy, straighten yourself up → *restructured behaviour*: 'Meg, I'm sorry. Let's make a list of what we need, and I'll go down to the shop right away.'

Getting out of the negative cycle

Reversing the negative cycle is not always simple or easy. Betty said that her thoughts crept up on her like prowling wolves, and before she knew it she was immersed in negativism.

Negative thinking is destructive and is wasteful of precious energy. Negative thinking often springs from a sense of inferiority and inadequacy, of low self-esteem and uncertainty. Self-confidence, on the other hand, leads to self-realisation and successful achievement. If your inner dialogue is made up of negative thoughts, stop them before they can find a roosting place in your hair.

How often have you had a summons to 'see the boss', or something similar? Then you found yourself thinking, 'Oh, my God! I'm for the high jump!' You worked yourself up into a state, maybe not being able to sleep or eat properly, only to discover that there was nothing sinister in the summons. You have allowed negative thinking to control your feelings and your behaviour.

You may think that there is nothing you can do, but you can – most certainly, if you really want to. Part of the process of change is deciding just how much negative thinking is a problem for you; how much it controls or influences your life.

CASE STUDY

David's story of successful thought change
David does a great deal of travelling for his company, which frequently involves several nights away from home. He develops a fear of sleeping in strange places. His obsessive worrying about overnight trips began about the time of the death of his wife. When preparing for bed in the hotel, David thinks about people using a master-key to enter his room while he is asleep. While planning his next business trip he becomes very tense anticipating the anxiety he will feel in the strange hotel. A counsellor introduces him to thought-stopping. This is an account of what he achieves.

1. He visualises unpacking in a strange room, thinking about plans for the next day, then going to bed.

2. He then imagines lying in darkness with the feeling that the door might swing ajar. In the middle of these thoughts the egg-timer that the counsellor has started up goes off. He shouts 'Stop!' and simultaneously snaps his fingers.

3. When the thought recurs before thirty seconds are up, he shouts, 'Stop!' again.

4. After succeeding with the shout, he begins saying 'Stop!' in a normal voice and then a whisper. Finally, he is able to shout 'Stop!' silently inside his head.

5. He has to repeat each phase several times before feeling that he can go on to the next one.

6. During the next three days, he uses a sub-audible 'Stop!' at the very beginning of each intrusive thought.

7. He also reinforces the command by snapping a rubber band which he wears around his wrist.

8. The thoughts decrease in frequency and only last a few moments when they occur.

9. By the next trip, he has markedly decreased the anxiety. He takes his tape recorder and sets it to say 'Stop' at intervals of five, ten, three and eight minutes during the time he is preparing for bed.

10. By the end of the trip, he is aware that he isn't thinking about the terrors of sleeping in strange places, but is much more focused on the challenges of his business.

MAKING THOUGHT-STOPPING WORK

Follow these points when using the thought-stopping technique:

- Failure with thought-stopping may mean that you have selected a thought that is very difficult to extinguish.

- Select an unwanted thought that is either less intrusive or less frightening than your initial choice.

- It is helpful to become proficient at the technique before tackling the more stressful obsessive or phobic thoughts.

- If the sub-vocalised 'Stop!' is not successful for you, and you find it embarrassing to say 'Stop!' aloud in public (and few of us wouldn't!), you can substitute the rubber band, or you might try pressing your finger nails into the palms of your hands to stop unwanted thoughts.

- Stopping a thought takes time. The thought will return and you will have to interrupt it again, possibly several times.

- The main effort is to stifle each thought just as it begins and to concentrate on something else. The thoughts will return less and less readily in most cases, and eventually cease to be a problem.

LEARNING TO EMPOWER YOURSELF AND OTHERS

Empowerment means believing that you can take control of what happens to you.

> **Empowerment means you believe that what you do, what you contribute, is important to yourself and other people.**

Needless to say, this concept is as far from some ideas about personal responsibility as the moon from the earth. It means taking a justifiable pride in yourself and your accomplishments and not being 'ever so humble.' It means not counting yourself to be less than anybody else, simply because you are different. Yet it is probably easier to hang on to the past – what we know – than it is to risk moving into the future – the unknown. If the space pioneers had put the dangers before the vision of space travel, there would have been no moon-walk.

Empowerment is forward looking; it does not mean hanging on to the past, however good that was. Empowerment means going for excellence. This does not mean being perfect. To be perfect means that we have arrived at some super-state of being and there is nothing left to achieve. Many of us are so caught up in the business of survival that we have no energy left for self-improvement. An empowered person is striving to leave the gravity-pull of the basic needs, to get launched into moving towards some future goal.

Empowerment may mean dramatic change, and change can be a painful experience – much like the feeling of loss – as old ways and patterns are replaced with new.

Empowering yourself and others

The following are ways you can work on your own empowerment, and empowered people encourage others to be empowered.

1. Become an effective communicator.

2. Aim to help others understand, rather than take it for granted that they do.

3. Respect people's confidences.

4. Be open with people and they will usually be open with you, but don't force openness.

5. Talk about what is important to other people, not what is important only to you.

6. When you make decisions and take action, make sure they don't conflict with other important parts of your life.

7. Delay making decisions which involve other people until you consult with them.

8. Empower others by telling them they are doing well and comment on how they take responsibility.

9. Empower others by helping to build their self-esteem.

10. Empower your children by discussing problems and look for longer-term solutions.

11. Empower others by always trying to inspire and set an example of empowerment.

12. Empower yourself by thinking of long-term success rather than immediate satisfaction.

13. Tell yourself that whatever your successes, you can achieve more.

14. Don't look back with regret, but look back to see how much you have grown and how valuable a person you are.

15. Try to understand why someone is not growing and do what-ever you can to help empower that person.

16. Empower others by valuing them as they are, not as their reputations indicate or as you hope they will be.

17. Empower others by believing them to be good and worthwhile and act towards them accordingly.

18. Have faith in the abilities of others, and demonstrate it.

19. Focus on strengths and assets rather than on mistakes and weaknesses.

20. Use empowerment as a powerful tool to fight anxiety.

ENCOURAGING ONE ANOTHER AND BUILDING RESPECT

Encouragement communicates trust, respect and belief. Many psychologists contend that there are only two basic human emotions: love and fear. Encouragement communicates caring and movement towards others – love – whereas discouragement results in lowered self-esteem and alienation from others – fear. Yet, despite the intention to be encouraging, all too often we discourage rather than encourage. An example is the manager or parent who 'lets things go' as long as they are going well, and who comments only when things go wrong.

A crucial start to being a more encouraging person is to become more aware of, and to eliminate, discouraging messages. Start using encouraging words that build people up. Figure 7 will give you some ideas.

SUMMARY

• Empowerment of yourself and others is one way of building self-esteem. A by-product is that anxiety is reduced in the process because you are taking control, but control in a healthy way, rather than trying to dominate others. Empowerment means appraising yourself positively, recognising your strengths and weaknesses, but building on strengths.

• The opposite of empowerment is impotence, and the associated meanings of weakness and failure. Empowerment means thinking positively, not irrationally or living in a fantasy world, but being realistic although also not allowing yourself to be defeated before something has ever happened.

EMPOWERING OTHERS BY SAYING . .

You do a good job of . . .
You have improved in . . .
I like (enjoy) you, but I don't like what you do.
You can help me (us, the others) by . . .
Let us try it together.
So you made a mistake; now, what can you learn from it?
You'd like me to think that you can't do it, but I think you can.
Keep trying; don't give up.
I am sure that you can straighten this out (solve this
     problem) but if you need any help, you know where
     you can find me.
I'm sure you will be able to handle it.

Fig. 7. Examples of words of encouragement.

- Empowering other people means believing in them, as much as you believe in yourself.

- If you do not empower yourself, you cannot empower other people.

- Encouraging one another is a sure way of empowering people.

- Empowered people have a powerful tool to fight anxiety. It is easy to discourage yourself by negative and defeatist self-talk. Learn to use self-talk that builds you up, not pulls you down, and learn to use words that encourage and build people up and in so doing, you will build yourself up.

12

Teaching Yourself Strategies to Combat Anxiety

Certain strategies have already been introduced. One, which may not be recognised as a strategy, is increasing your understanding of what anxiety is.

> **Information enlightens; understanding empowers, and the evidence of empowerment is the positive changes you make in your life**.

The aim of this book is that information will be absorbed, inwardly digested and help to sustain you in difficult times. If you suffer from anxiety, then hopefully you will have taken heart from the case studies cited here, for they represent a wide range of people who have learnt, to one degree or another, to manage their anxiety.

WORKING TO MAINTAIN, NOT SQUANDER, YOUR ENERGY

Anxiety drains energy. Why? Because anxiety focuses more on what might be than what is. Anxiety is a negative force that pulls you off-centre. It disturbs your waking thoughts, and confronts you when you are asleep or trying to get to sleep.

Chapter 1 discussed anxiety as a treadmill. Certain animals, hamsters and mice seem to enjoy running in their treadmill. Do you? Would you, if you were forced into it, and made to keep running until you dropped from sheer exhaustion, and then were whipped until you dragged yourself up and again wearily turned the heavy wheel? This is the trap of anxiety. You are the prisoner. You keep *yourself* running. Something within you keeps driving you, pushing you on, without respite. Determine today to change all that, to challenge the gaoler within, to start to take control. Get off the treadmill and start living.

Can you wonder that you have no energy if your life is a constant treadmill? Do you dwell on the past so much that you destroy happiness in the present? Or, do you anticipate events so much that your feelings are in a constant whirl of anticipation of something dreadful that might happen? Both living in the past and in the future drain energy from the present. Can you wonder you feel tired? Energy is finite. We can harness it, or we can squander it.

What you can do to generate energy

- Believe in yourself.

- Be interested in what you are doing.

- Be enthusiastic about what you are doing.

- Keep company as often as you can with people who think positively.

- Find an emotional 'garage' where you can recharge your batteries.

- Be organised, so that conflict between competing forces is reduced to a minimum.

- Don't spent eighty per cent of your energy to get twenty per cent result.

- Don't abuse your body, mind and emotions.

- Don't engage in futile regrets.

- Don't live your life being angry with yourself and others.

- Don't forget to rest: even an elephant sleeps.

- Sleep when you can, and when you want to.

- If you are a tortoise, don't pretend to be a hare. If you drive constantly in the fast lane, you run the danger of being run over by others faster than you are.

- If you rush to get things done, slow down and tell yourself, 'There–is–plenty–of–time.'

- If your energy is being drained by guilt, study Chapter 6. If you need to make reparation, do it now. If you don't have to, don't keep punishing yourself.

- Is your energy being drained by fear? Is this fear of something you can change? If it is, then do something about it. If not, then it is unrealistic and you are allowing a mirage to control you. Transform the mirage into something real, then you can learn to handle it.

- Give yourself a change of outlook. If you work in an office, do something manual; if your work is manual, do something to challenge your intellect.

- Listen to inspirational music and read something inspirational every day.

USING RELAXATION TO COMBAT ANXIETY

Relaxation quietens our physical and psychological internal worlds and, therefore, aids in reducing our anxiety level. One can relax immediately and quickly by starting to breathe slowly and deeply. There are many tapes around which teach relaxation.

Trying a relaxation technique

A simple technique is to concentrate on one specific part of the body, for example the index finger. Keep the concentration fixed on it, and mentally keep telling it to relax. After a time you will discover that not only is the finger relaxed, but the whole arm, and gradually the feeling of heaviness will extend all over the body. This sort of focused relaxation can be done anywhere; sitting on a train or bus, or any other situation where it is not practicable to lie down on the floor and carry out full relaxation. This can be very energising.

USING AUTOSUGGESTION TO COMBAT ANXIETY

The practice of positive thinking in the treatment of physical symptoms and anxiety was popularised by Emil Coué around the turn of this century. Coué asserted that all of our thoughts become reality: We are what we think we are. If we think sad thoughts, we feel unhappy; if we think anxious thoughts, we become tense. When we predict that we are going to be lonely and miserable, it is likely our prediction will come true, because our negative thoughts will be reflected in behaviour which isolates us from people. This turns into a self-fulfilling prophecy.

Coué recommended to his patients that they repeat twenty times to themselves on waking, mechanically moving their lips, the now-famous phrase:

- Every day in every way I am getting better and better

USING IMAGINATION TO COMBAT ANXIETY

Imagination is effective in treating many anxiety-related and physical illnesses, including headaches, muscle spasms, chronic pain and anxiety. Some people seem to have a natural gift for creating inner images. If you are one of these, using imagery is likely to prove very rewarding for you. For many of us, the imagination we were born with has been overlaid with intellectual data. Careful nurturing and use will help it to resurface.

1. Find a quiet spot, sit comfortably. Rest your hands on your thighs. Ensure that your head is supported. Close your eyes if you wish.

2. Imagine a situation which is stressful for you. Feel the tension in your body, in your breathing. Feel your palms beginning to sweat. Feel the tightening of the stomach muscles.

3. Notice all the details of the unpleasant situation: sight, smell, sound, how you are dressed, what is said, by whom and the tone of voice.

4. Feel the discomfort of the event. Feel the emotions: anger, fear, sadness, worthlessness. Do not avoid them – experience them.

5. Now push yourself to change what you are experiencing. Feel the anger being replaced with irritation, or annoyance; feel the fear being replaced with concern or disappointment. Change the emotion into one you can handle comfortably.

6. Your mind may tell you that it can't be done. It *can*. Your mind is trying to trick you into doing what it wants. It doesn't want to give up power and control.

7. When you have changed one emotion, take another look at what is happening in your body. You have become more relaxed; your breathing has slowed; you are no longer sweating; you feel calm.

8. Now say to yourself: *I am in control, not my mind.* Don't let your mind argue with you. Remember, you are what you believe.

9. Now let your imagination take you somewhere pleasant and comfortable. Don't plan what to do, just let it happen. This is your retreat, your private place, which only you can enter. When you feel under pressure, in your imagination return to this place. Now give it a name and use this name often. Even just saying the name will take you back and you will feel more able to cope with the pressures around you.

10. Whenever you have used imagination, stand up slowly and gently move your limbs, walk around and feel yourself fully relaxed. Check the time on your watch or on the clock. Touch a few objects to ground you in the present.

USING MUSIC TO COMBAT ANXIETY

Make an uninterrupted tape entitled My Relaxing Music. Repeated listening to the same music that helped you relax in the past carries with it a positive association that is likely to be beneficial now and in the future.

Get into a comfortable position and close your eyes. Allow yourself to flow with the music. Where does it take you? What images spontaneously come to you? What feelings arise within you? Learn to live in peace with your imagination.

USING COLOURS TO COMBAT ANXIETY

Every colour has a distinct psychological quality of its own, and consequently a definite effect. The so-called 'cold' and subdued colours have a quieting effect, and warm, vivid, and bright colours have a stimulating or exciting influence.

Certain shades of blue are usually considered as having a soothing, harmonising effect; light green is refreshing; red and bright yellow are usually stimulating, while pink suggests serenity and happiness. Identify what colours relax you and which create anxiety.

Make up some cards using the following colours and use them as meditations. Place them about one foot from your eyes, and while you gaze at them, let the colours blend with your thoughts about what the words mean.

- Calmness: dark green

- Joy: yellow

- Love: blue

- Serenity: deep blue.

SLEEPING BETTER AND REDUCING ANXIETY

Try following these points to reduce anxiety:

1. Avoid situations that leave you filled with regret and tensions.
2. Do the same thing every night before bedtime.
3. Don't get too keyed up before going to bed. Remember, nobody has been known to die from not being able to sleep.
4. Learn to relax your mind as well as your body.
5. Meditation or prayer before going to bed will help to relax your mind.
6. Plan variety into your day.
7. Within reason, stick to the same waking and sleeping hours as much as possible.

USING EXERCISE TO COMBAT ANXIETY

Exercise is one of the simplest and most effective means of reducing anxiety. Vigorous physical exertion is the natural outlet for your body when it is in the fight or flight state of arousal. After exercise your body chemistry returns to its normal equilibrium and you feel relaxed and refreshed.

There are two broad categories of exericse: aerobic exercise and low intensity exercises.

1. Aerobic exercise involves sustained, rhythmic activity of the large muscle groups, especially the legs. Popular aerobic exercises are running, jogging, brisk walking, swimming, bicycling and dancing.

2. Low intensity exercise is not vigorous or prolonged enough to produce the training effect. It can be used to increase muscle strength, and flexibility and joint mobility. However, it does not provide much benefit to your cardiovascular system. Examples of low intensity exercise are slow walking, house cleaning, shopping, office duties and light gardening.

Research is just beginning to explain why exercise is effective in reducing general anxiety and depression. It is known that fifteen to twenty minutes of vigorous exercise stimulates certain chemicals which influence mood, and stimulate endorphins – natural painkillers and mood elevators.

Exercise, especially in competitive sports, is a good outlet for stressful emotions such as anger and irritability. There is conflicting evidence about jogging, however. Some researchers maintain that jogging, particularly on hard pavements, increases joint strain. Take advice from experts before you embark on an exercise schedule.

CHANGING THE WAY YOU BREATHE TO COMBAT ANXIETY

Shallow breathing is often associated with anxiety. Learning to breathe effectively could be your first step toward combating anxiety. Some of the yoga breathing exercises are excellent and easy to use. A wonderful method of breathing for releasing anxiety is 'bellows breathing'.

- Bellows breathing starts not in the nose, but in the throat. Open your mouth and breathe fairly deeply: you will hear a noise like a bellows.

- After you have heard the noise, and while you are still breathing in, close your lips and continue breathing. You will discover that you are breathing with that same noise.

- You will notice that the air enters your lungs much lower than if you merely breathe through your nostrils.

- When you exhale, try to keep the bellows going for about one minute at a time.

- Get the breath well down in the abdomen on every cycle.

NUGGETS TO LIVE YOUR LIFE BY

- We must feel love within ourselves before we can give it to others.

- Our minds cannot tell the difference between real and imaginary experiences.

- Imagine success and not failure.

- Quality not quantity of our contributions determines the rewards we receive.

- Improving your vocabulary increases confidence to interact with people.

- Achieving a goal means being clear about what your goal is.

- Physical contact speaks louder than words.

- Children deprived of physical contact grow up to be deprived adults.

- Play out a positive self-fulfilling prophecy, not a negative one.

- The body is the channel for what is harboured in the mind.

- If you don't adapt, frequently, the rut will close over you.

- If you are still green, you are still growing: dead things have stopped growing.

- Do something no one else is willing to do and you will be a winner.

SUMMING UP

Epilogue

Writing this book has been very rewarding as well as demanding. I have a fervent belief in what I am writing and I trust this fervency has come through to you.

A writer never sees the audience, yet must always try to make emotional contact with them. Many of you may be experiencing anxiety yourselves, or you want to learn how to avoid it, or help someone who suffers from it. I hope what you have read has touched a chord within you and that, above all, you will find hope. I set out to write a book which contributes to the knowledge of what anxiety is and to give some strategies to help combat it. Upon these two bases we have looked at anxiety from many angles, which broadly could be put into three connected boxes: thinking, feeling and behaviour.

If you can pass on some of the principles and concepts to six other people, then you will have demonstrated that you are taking control of your own anxiety, as well as making a contribution to changing the little bit of the world in which you live. For the moments when we are emotionally involved with others, through caring, listening, or simply being there for them, our own problems are temporarily forgotten.

Summary of the book

- The emphasis throughout the book has been that although anxiety in its extreme may be crippling, you can learn strategies to cope with it. If you can live just five minutes free from anxiety, then it is possible to increase this, bit by bit, so that more of your day is anxiety-free.

- Because anxiety seems to be a universal plague, none of us is exempt from it. While some people seem never to suffer from it, that does not mean that those of us who do are weaklings. In fact, it could be said that because we have learned to cope with anxiety, and are yet able to get on with our lives in spite of it, we are the stronger. Certainly living with such a crippling condition gives a degree of compassion and understanding for other sufferers, something which non-sufferers would not necessarily understand.

- One of the important factors of controlling anxiety is to recognise what makes it worse and then what eases it. Finding strategies that work for you is important.

- At the same time as identifying the anxiety triggers, and useful strategies, it is important not to deliberately court anxiety situations if we can avoid them. To do so is a bit like indulging in certain foods we know we are allergic to and then rushing off to the doctor for medication. A person who has been diagnosed as diabetic must remain on a strict diet; an alcoholic must never let alcohol pass the lips again. If either person transgressed, we might call them stupid. If we allow ourselves to get into anxiety-provoking situations which we could avoid, then we are not being responsible to ourselves.

- One of the ways in which we can increase anxiety is neglecting to care for ourselves – to use the old adage, burning the candle at both ends. If we find we need a good eight hours sleep a night, and we consistently have less than this and do not give ourselves enough rest time, we are depleting the body of its essential reserves.

- An engine runs on fuel, so does the body. Make sure you give your body the correct fuel, and that you keep in good shape by appropriate rest as well as exercise.

- Breathing is the vital function that keeps you alive. Learn all you can about correct breathing and how it can help you combat anxiety.

- Nobody can cure your anxiety for you, and you might not be able to cure it yourself, but at least you can learn to manage it. Manage does not mean fighting it, but accepting that this is part of you, like any other long-term illness. The person with diabetes knows that it is not going to pass or get better. So with anxiety. By learning to cope more effectively you can live your life more fully.

- Don't let people tell you to 'pull yourself together'. If it were as easy as that you would have done so long ago. It is insulting and patronising. People with any inkling of what it is like to be in the grip of anxiety would never say that. If you know someone who suffers in this way, try to think how you might feel if you lived your life on the edge of a volcano that could erupt at any moment, or you were in the grip of an obsession that controlled every minute of your day.

- People with anxiety long for the periods of normality which rise out of the bleakness of their lives like islands rising out of a tempestuous sea, upon which they can stand and regain their strength.

- Finally, although the emphasis has been on what sufferers can do for themselves, others are prepared to help, but often they won't know what help is needed unless they are told. For those of us who may care for anxiety sufferers, let us bear in mind that when they are caught in the grip of acute anxiety they often lack the will to do things. So anything we can do, however small, to relieve the anxiety will help the person more than we could ever know. If we offer help to someone, let us be certain that we are not offering it out of pity, for that will be perceived as patronising. Let our help be given from a grateful heart that we can reach out and touch someone at their point of need.

Glossary

Agoraphobia. Abnormal fear of being helpless in an embarrassing situation from which one cannot escape; characterised especially by the avoidance of open or public places.

Ambivalence. Simultaneous and contradictory attitudes or feelings (as attraction and repulsion) towards an object, person or action; continual fluctuation between one thing and its opposite, uncertainty as to which approach to follow.

Anorexia nervosa. An eating disorder characterised by refusal or inability to maintain minimum normal weight for age and height, combined with intense and irrational fear of gaining weight.

Anxiety. Apprehension, tension or uneasiness from anticipation of danger, the source of which is largely unknown or un-recognised.

Anxiety management training. This is not a specific training, but a number of techniques which the sufferer can use to reduce an attack. These may be: rhythmic breathing, desensitisation therapy, relaxation, cognitive restructuring. Counselling is also used to help the person understand the underlying factors of anxiety.

Autonomic nervous system. The part of the nervous system outside the conscious control that stimulates the cardio-vascular, digestive, reproductive and respiratory organs.

Behaviour therapy. A mode of treatment that focuses on modifying observable behaviour and thoughts that relate to behaviour.

Body image. The inner sense one has of one's self and body.

Bulimia nervosa. An eating disorder characterised by recurrent episodes of binge-eating followed by compensatory behaviour such as purging or other methods to control weight.

Cognition. The act or process of knowing, including both aware-ness and judgment.

Cognitive restructuring therapy. Cognition means 'of the mind'. Cognitive restructuring means helping people correct habitual errors in thinking. It is particularly helpful in anxiety and depression where the aim is to change negative to positive thinking.

Compulsion. Repetitive and ritualistic behaviour such as hand-washing, arranging things in order or counting. The aim is to prevent or reduce distress, or prevent some dreadful event happening.

Defence mechanisms. Unconscious adjustments made, either through action or the avoidance of action, to keep from recognising personal qualities or motives that might lower self-esteem or heighten anxiety.

Delusion. A delusion is a persistent false belief which is both untrue and that cannot be shaken by reason or contradictory evidence, and which is inconsistent with the person's knowledge or culture.

Depression. A disorder of mood marked especially by sadness, inactivity, difficulty in thinking and concentration, a significant increase or decrease in appetite and time spent sleeping, feelings of dejection and hopelessness, and sometimes suicidal tendencies. **Reactive depression** is said to be attributable to a specific event, such as death. **Clinical or endogenous depression**: both these terms have been replaced by mood disorders, although some people still use them. Clinical depression refers to a depression which is serious enough to need treatment by a doctor. Endogenous means arising from within. In older textbooks the distinction was made between reactive and endogenous, the latter being more serious.

Desensitisation therapy. This is where the person is exposed gradually to whatever creates anxiety. It is also used in treating allergies. The person is exposed, under relaxed conditions, to a series of stimuli that increasingly approximate to the anxiety-provoking one, until the stimuli no longer produce anxiety.

Distress. Where stress has accumulated to the degree where normal coping mechanisms no longer function. The person has become emotionally exhausted.

Down's syndrome. Also known as trisomy 21, a common form of mental handicap caused by an abnormality in the chromosomes; formerly known as mongolism, because of the mongoloid features of people with this disorder.

Dyspareunia. Persistent pain during sexual intercourse.

Eating disorder. Marked disturbance in eating behaviour. It includes anorexia nervosa, bulimia nervosa, and binge-eating.

Eating disorders are associated with an overwhelming concern about body weight and feeling and looking excessively fat.

Electrocardiogram. The record produced by an electro-cardiograph; a tracing representing the heart's electrical action.

Empathy. The action of understanding, being aware of, being sensitive to, and getting in touch with the feelings, thoughts and experience of another.

Endorphins. Any of a group of hormone-like substances with pain-killing and tranquillising properties that are secreted by the brain.

Euphoria. An exaggerated feeling of physical and emotional well-being, usually of psychological origin, not attributable to some external event.

Fight/flight response. The term given to the action of certain hormones within the body which prepares the person to fight or run away from danger.

Flashback. A past incident recurring vividly in the mind, often associated with previous taking of hallucinogen-type drugs, but also with horrific experiences.

Free-floating anxiety. Severe, generalised, persistent anxiety not specifically ascribed to a particular object or event, and often a messenger of panic.

Homeostasis. The tendency towards a relatively stable equilibrium between interdependent elements. An example in the body is the way temperature is maintained.

Hypochondriasis. A morbid concern about one's health, especially when accompanied by delusions of physical disease.

Hypothalamus. A small but very important structure located just above the brain stem and just below the thalamus. Considered a part of the central core of the brain, it includes centres that govern motivated behaviour such as eating, drinking, sex and emotions. It also regulates endocrine activity and maintains body homeostasis.

Impotence. The inability to achieve or maintain an erection of sufficient quality to engage in successful intercourse.

Insomnia. Prolonged and usually abnormal inability to obtain adequate sleep.

Mood. A prevailing and sustained emotion or feeling.

Obsession. Recurring or persistent thoughts, ruminations, images, or impulses which seem to invade a person's consciousness despite all attempts to ignore, suppress or control them.

Obsessional compulsive disorder (OCD). An anxiety disorder characterised by obsessions, compulsions, or both, that are time-consuming and interfere significantly with normal routine, occupational functioning, usual social activities or relationships with others.

Oedipus complex. In psychoanalytic theory, the positive libidinal (sexual) feelings of a child towards the parent of the opposite sex, and hostile or jealous feelings toward the parent of the same sex that may be a source of adult personality disorder when unresolved. Electra complex is when it occurs in females.

Palpitation. A heartbeat that is unusually rapid, strong or irregular enough to make a person aware of it – usually over 120 per minute, as opposed to the normal of 60 to 100 per minute.

Panic attack. Sudden, overpowering fright, a feeling of unreasoning terror.

Phallic stage. In psychoanalytic theory, the period of psychosexual development from about 2½ to 6 years during which sexual interest, curiosity and pleasurable experience in boys centre on the penis, and in girls to a lesser extent on the clitoris.

Phobia. An exaggerated, usually inexplicable and illogical fear of a particular object, class of objects or situation.

Pituitary gland. The master gland of the endocrine system situated at the base of the brain, so called because it controls hormone production of other endocrine glands.

Post-traumatic stress disorder. An anxiety disorder in which exposure to an exceptional mental or physical stressor is followed, sometimes immediately and sometimes not until three months or more after the incident, by persistent re-experiencing of the event, with its associated feelings and behaviours.

Rhythmic breathing. This is also called 'tidal breathing'. It means controlling the breathing to regular counts. Example: breathe in to the count of four; hold for the count of two; breathe out to the count of four; hold to the count of two. Such breathing helps to bring a sense of calmness.

Self-esteem. A confidence and satisfaction in oneself, self-respect.

Separation anxiety. A disorder occurring in children before the age of 18 years, consisting of inappropriate anxiety about being separated from home or from persons to whom the child is attached.

Social phobia. The irrational fear and avoidance of being in a situation in which a person's activities could be watched.

Stress. An imprecise term, but generally taken to mean a state of psychological tension produced by the kinds of forces or pressures (stressors) with which the person feels unable to cope.

Syndrome. A group of signs and symptoms that occur together and characterise a particular abnormality.

Tachycardia. Abnormally rapid heart rate, usually taken to be over 100 beats per minute.

Testosterone. A male hormone that is produced by the testes or made synthetically. Its chief function is to stimulate the development of the male reproductive organs, including the prostate, and for inducing and maintaining male secondary sex characteristics. It encourages growth of bone and muscle and helps maintain muscle strength.

Vaginismus. A recurrent or persistent, powerful and involuntary spasm of the pelvic musculature constricting the vagina so that penetration is painful or impossible.

Voluntary nervous system. This is the system of sensory and motor nerves which control the muscles of the body, and thereby all voluntary movement. Sensory messages from all parts of the body are sorted in the spinal cord and sent to the brain to be analysed and acted upon.

Further Reading

A Woman in Your Own Right, A. Dickson (Quartet Books, 1982).

A-Z of Counselling Theory and Practice, William Stewart (Stanley Thornes, 1997, 2nd edition).

Building Self-Esteem: How to replace self-doubt with confidence and well-being, William Stewart (How to Books, 1998).

Comprehensive Textbook of Psychiatry/V, H. I. Kaplan and B. J. S. Sadock (eds), (Williams & Wilkins, 1995).

Counselling in Rehabilitation, William Stewart (Croom Helm, 1985).

How to Stop Worrying and Start Living, Dale Carnegie (The World's Work Ltd, 1948, and edited by Dorothy Carnegie, 1990).

Imagery and Symbolism in Counselling, William Stewart (Jessica Kingsley, 1996).

Learning to Counsel: How to develop the skills to work effectively with others, Jan Sutton and William Stewart (How To Books, 1997).

Prescription for Anxiety, Leslie D. Weatherhead (Hodder and Stoughton, 1956).

Self Help for your Nerves, Claire Weekes (Angus and Robertson Publishers, 1962).

Stop Feeling Tired and Start Living, Dora Albert (A. Thomas & Co., 1960).

The Power of Positive Thinking, Norman Vincent Peale (Cedar, 1953).

The Relaxation and Stress Reduction Workbook, Martha Davis, Elizabeth Robbins Eshelman, Matthew McKay (New Harbinger Publications, 1982).

Thriving on Stress: How to build confidence and make pressures work for you, Jan Sutton (How To Books, 1998).

'Free yourself from guilt', Beth Levine (*Reader's Digest* September 1997).

Useful Addresses

The Institute of Counselling, 6 Dixon Street, Glasgow G1 4AX. Tel: (0141) 204 2230. Fax: (0141) 221 2841. In addition to many distance learning counselling courses, the Institute offers Psychology for Counsellors, and An Introduction to Stress Management which includes a relaxation instruction tape.

British Association for Counselling, 1 Regent Place, Rugby, Warwickshire CV21 2PJ. Tel: (01788) 550899. The BAC produces a directory of counsellors and their particular interests.

Centre for Stress Management, 156 Westcombe Hill, London SE3 7DH. Tel: (020) 8293 4114.

Institute of Family Therapy, 43 Cavendish Street, London W1M 7RN. Tel: (020) 7935 1651. Family therapy: working with families experiencing psychological, behavioural and relationship problems.

RELATE Marriage Guidance, National Headquarters, Herbert Gray College, Little Church Street, Rugby CV21 3AP. Tel: (01788) 573241. Counselling for relationship problems; sexual problems (some branches). For local branches see under RELATE in local phone book.

Westminster Pastoral Foundation Counselling, 23 Kensington Square, London W8 5HN. Tel: (020) 7937 6956. Provides a professional service of counselling/psychotherapy.

Eating Disorders Association, First Floor, Wensun House, 103 Prince of Wales Road, Norwich, Norfolk NR1 1DW.

SOURCES OF LOCAL INFORMATION

1. GP practices will have details of local services available.

2. *Yellow Pages* – look under section Counselling and Advice.

3. Citizens Advice Bureau.

4. Councils of Community Service.

5. Local newspapers often provide a list of helpline telephone numbers.

Index